NNA LARDENT
ow of—Bernard

OMAS   FRANCES
KINSON = DE BRISSAC
ain R.N.   1760–1854
4–1828

EV.   ANNE   ANNE   REV. ARTHUR   GEORGE   ELIZABETH   JOSEPH
PTIMUS   DICKINSON   DICKINSON = BENONI EVANS   DICKINSON   DICKINSON = PHELPS
VER   d. in infancy   1791–1883   1793–1843   1797–1876   1791–1876
ost of Eton
–1852   11 children

SEBASTIAN
DICKINSON
1787   ANNE   REV. ARTHUR   GEORGE   EMMA   JOHN
Killed at Badajos 1811   EVANS   EVANS   EVANS   EVANS = WADDINGTON
            1820–1870   1822–1852   1825–1847   HUBBARD

                                                5 children

(1) HARRIET ANN DICKINSON = SIR JOHN EVANS, K.C.B. = (2) FRANCES PHELPS
       1823–1858   1823–1908   1826–1890

ILLIAM   = (3) MARIA MILLINGTON
CKINSON   LATHBURY
21–1832   1856–1944

HN   THOMAS   HARRY
RET   GORDON   KENDALL
INSON   DICKINSON   DICKINSON   JOAN EVANS
–1896   1862–1908   1867–1872   1893–

THUR   MARGARET   PHILIP   ADA   HARRIET   CHARLES
VANS = FREEMAN   NORMAN   DICKINSON   ANN   JAMES
–1941   EVANS   = GILBERT   EVANS = LONGMAN
                 1854–1893   1857–1938   1852–1934

                                                        4 children

           LEWIS EVANS = (1) BERYL MARY   ALICE   WILLIAM
           1853–1930   WARD   EVANS = MINET
                  = (2) EVA BRADFORD   1856–1882   1851–1933
                      1866–1928

                                        one daughter

JOHN DICKINSON   4 daughters
EVANS
1903–

THE ENDLESS WEB

BUST OF JOHN DICKINSON
by Baron Marochetti, 1850

THE
ENDLESS WEB

JOHN DICKINSON & CO. LTD
1804–1954

BY

JOAN EVANS

JONATHAN CAPE

THIRTY BEDFORD SQUARE · LONDON

First Published 1955

PRINTED IN ENGLAND AT THE CURWEN PRESS, PLAISTOW, E.13
ILLUSTRATIONS PRINTED BY CLARKE & SHERWELL LTD., NORTHAMPTON
BOUND BY A. W. BAIN & CO. LTD., LONDON

The following papers have been used in the manufacture of this book:

TEXT PAPER: Croxley Antique Wove
22½″ × 35″/64 lb. 516s

ILLUSTRATIONS: Croxley Photogravure
Printing
22½″ × 35″/64 lb. 516s

JACKET: Evensyde Offset (Smooth Finish)
23″ × 36″/80 lb. 500s

The text is set in Monotype Caslon Old Face, based on the first set of type punches cut by William Caslon the first, in the year 1722

CONTENTS

ILLUSTRATIONS

ILLUSTRATIONS

INTRODUCTION

In this book you will find a story of an enterprise whose roots grow deep in the British countryside. It owes its origin to a very remarkable man. John Dickinson learned his trade through the opportunities which came to him in his early years as a merchant of paper.

He set up in business in the City of London on his own account in 1804. Five years later he entered the field of paper manufacture and he acquired his first mill in the valley of the River Gade, in the beautiful county of Hertfordshire. From this point his story exemplifies the striving, endurance and initiative which have made the basis of British industry. Surely, irresistibly, inexorably, the development has gone on. The pattern is typical of the amazing developments in the world's progress which had their genesis in the British industrial revolution.

John Dickinson was essentially a man of iron determination and courageous vision. His first venture involved years of strenuous effort, and a steadfast refusal to admit defeat by the initial difficulties and disappointments. Then the foundations were laid on which the structure of the business was to be erected, and the first signs of success appeared. From then onward, the story of John Dickinson clearly follows the principle that 'Success succeeds when used for future needs'. Each development is seen to be part of a co-ordinated plan and each successive step emanates from a previous accomplishment.

To the memory of such men we pay our tribute with feelings of intense gratitude. They were the pioneers. They provided for our predecessors and for us both the material shape of things capable of development and the spiritual force which came of their personalities and their faith that they were destined to play a great and worthy part in their country's history. In the House of Dickinson we believe that the spirit of our Founder lives on, and that it is a never-dying inspiration to all who serve beneath the 'Lion Brand' banner—our trade mark.

The picture which is given in the book of the Dickinsons and of the Pratt Barlows and the Evanses, who are so closely linked with the story, is in itself a fascinating record of a bygone age. We are indeed fortunate that Dr. Joan Evans, despite the innumerable calls upon her time, has undertaken the task of writing this book. As a great-niece of John Dickinson, much of the firm's history is, also, her personal family story. It is fitting that a talented descendant of the paper-maker who made this account possible, should commit to paper the record of developments related to the Dickinson production of paper and paper products.

The record is a tribute to all men and women who, in the past, have taken their share in building the House of Dickinson, and it will, both now and in the future, serve as an inspiration to all who strive to build a superstructure worthy of the impregnable foundation work of previous generations. We would also wish the book to be interpreted as a grateful gesture to all our friends, throughout the world, who support Dickinson's in many ways in great and growing measure.

Finally, we accept unreservedly the rightness of the principle that it is the duty of Industry to serve with singleness of aim and with all its might, the interests of the Customers, its Workers, its Shareholders. We believe that the rightness of these principles, which we have inherited, and their application over the years, is the simple fact why, one hundred and fifty years after the founding of the Dickinson business, we can present a phase of a never-ending story—the story of the Endless Web.

J. W. RANDALL
Chairman

Apsley Mills,
Hemel Hempstead.

The outworn rags, the written word, the news of yesteryear,
The margins cut from the clean sheet that once spread wide and fair,
Cleansed by terrestrial acids, bleached by human tears from grime,
Come to be pulped by the inexorable wheels of Time.
Sweetened by heavenly waters, beaten in the mills of strife,
Assoiled once more they spread upon the endless web of Life.

J.E.

Rags make Paper,
Paper makes Money,
Money makes Banks,
Banks make Loans,
Loans make Beggars,
Beggars make Rags.

EIGHTEENTH CENTURY

PREFACE

My qualification for writing this book is that I am the daughter of John Evans, the nephew of John Dickinson who joined the firm in 1840. I was born at Nash Mills House, and spent my childhood there in close proximity to the Mills. My father had retired from their Chairmanship in 1885, yet they still formed as natural a part of the world of Nash House as did the laundry or the stables. My dolls used to be mended in the Engineering Department; I had the freedom of the Mills, and liked to spend my Saturdays among the glorious piles of *Illustrated London News* waiting to be pulped, from which I gained my first notions of English history. I used to go to tea with Mr. Leonard Stephenson, the firm's first engineer and once an apprentice to Stephenson of the 'Rocket'; he lived in retirement in a cottage John Dickinson had built at the drive's end. My father, as a retired Chairman, was punctilious in never entering the Mills during working hours; but he liked to walk round on Saturdays and to talk of old times to the watchman, and sometimes to me as I tagged along behind him. The clank of the loose cast-iron grids of the Nash Mills wharf sounds still in my memory.

When I began to write this book I did not know that the diaries of John Dickinson's wife and elder daughter were in existence. His great-grand-daughter, my cousin Mrs. Lowry Cole, made them available to me, and they are the chief source for the earlier chapters of this book. For me it has been strange and moving to read in Ann Dickinson's journals of the fruit trees and laburnums she planted at Nash Mills, for they were familiar in my childhood; the cupboards she had had made held my clothes and toys; the lamps she bought were lighting her diaries as I read them. I danced as a girl with the grand-children of the

xv

people who called on her, and knew every lane and common by which she drove in the gig, the chaise and the carriage. The square garden at Nash Mills was my childhood's kingdom. It was tended long enough to give its flowers for my half-brother's funeral in 1941, but is now demolished. It is perhaps time that I—one of the last links with its beginning—should write what I remember and what I have learned of the history of John Dickinson and his family, that in all its generations came back to that house and that garden as to home.

I am no less indebted to my nephew, John Dickinson Evans, who sent me from Kenya the relevant family papers in his possession. My niece Sibyl Longman, my cousins Josephine Phelps and Robert Pratt Barlow and Ann Dickinson's great-nephew Colonel Charles Grover, have been no less kind in putting material at my disposal. I have been able to avail myself of the recollections of Mr. W. A. Stephenson and Mr. J. W. Timberlake and on minor points have availed myself of the knowledge of Miss Gladys Scott Thomson, Dr. John Johnson, Mr. L. S. Pressnell, Mr. A. Jenkinson, Mr. F. J. T. Heckford, and other members of the staff. The Board of Directors has most liberally permitted me access even to confidential papers. The Chairman, Mr. J. W. Randall, has kindly read my book in manuscript and has provided it with an introduction; and I am greatly indebted to the Managers of the Mills and to Mr. C. J. Mearing, for their kindness in answering my questions and aiding me in the search for illustrations.

J. E.

Wotton-under-Edge
1954

I . GEORGE LONGMAN

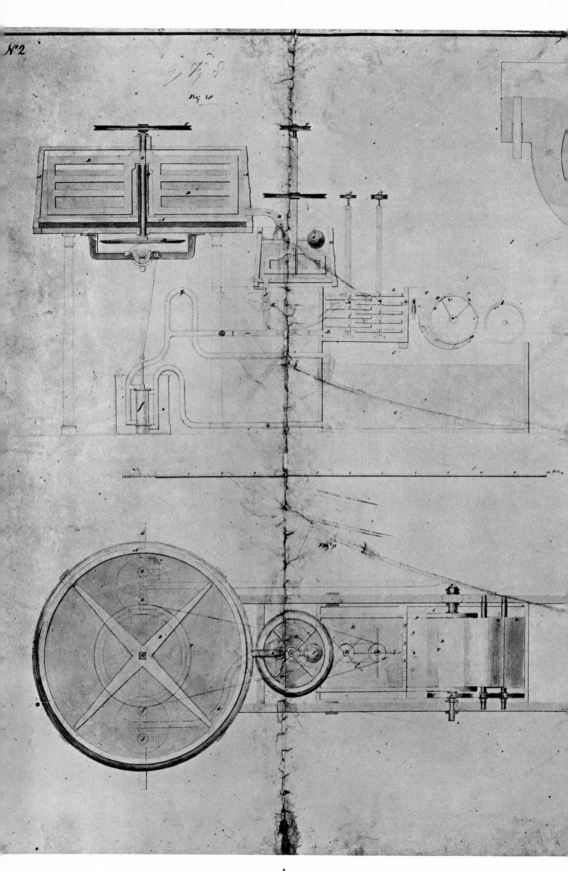

2. JOHN DICKINSON'S PAPER-MAKING MACHINE

I

JOHN DICKINSON

1804–1809

JOHN DICKINSON was born on 29 March 1782, the eldest
son of Captain Thomas Dickinson, R.N., who had lately succeeded his father as Superintendent of the Ordnance Trans-
ports at Woolwich, with quarters in the Tower of London.[1]
John's grandfather,[2] after whom he was named, had run away
to sea as a schoolboy from his native Northumberland, and had
risen to the rank of Captain in the Royal Navy during the
Napoleonic Wars, fighting the French in the *Brunswick*. His
patron, Lord Townshend (whose Irish governess he had married)
had given him promotion in the Ordnance Department, and
towards the end of his life he had been elected an Elder Brother
of Trinity House.

John Dickinson's mother was Frances de Brissac, a woman of
pure Huguenot descent and great energy of character. Fanny
Burney the novelist—then Madame d'Arblay—met the Thomas
Dickinsons on a country holiday in the summer of 1798. She
describes Captain Dickinson as 'very shy, but seems a sensible

[1] I have written more fully of the Dickinsons in *Time and Chance*,
1943, p. 17 *et sqq.*

[2] A family tradition affirms a connexion between this John
Dickinson, born near Alnwick in 1723, and the American John
Dickinson, born in Pennsylvania in 1732, who opposed the Declaration
of Independence but signed the Federal Constitution. Mr. John H.
Powell of Philadelphia kindly informs me that the family of the
American Dickinson had been settled for three generations in Penn-
sylvania, and the connexion, if any, must have been remote, in spite of
the family resemblance discernible in their portraits.

man' and goes on to say that 'his lady is open, chatty, fond of her children, and anxious to accomplish them'.[1]

John Dickinson's ancestry was thus mixed: half Huguenot, a quarter North-country, and a quarter Irish. He seems to have inherited little from Ireland but a hot temper, but to have combined North-country shrewdness with the Huguenot capacity for hard work, thrift and attention to detail. His mother was indubitably the dominant of his parents; she brought him up to be hospitable and splendour-loving as well as of complete integrity in practical things.

It was she who introduced him into the world of commerce. Her father had been one of the French silk-weavers of Spitalfields and had made friends about 1767 with another Londoner, Andrew Strahan, then a young man of seventeen or eighteen. Strahan's uncle had been publisher to Johnson, Hume, Gibbon and other great writers of the time.[2] He, in his turn, with his brother George and his partner John Spottiswoode, who married his sister, carried on the business and became the King's Printer; he also sat in Parliament from 1796 to 1820. He remained on terms of the closest friendship with Frances Dickinson and her family and counted as an adopted relation. When Fanny Burney met the Dickinsons in 1798 he was of the party. She wrote to her sister: 'He has all the appearance of a very worthy, sensible, unpretending man, well-bred and good-natured. Long connected with the Dickinsons, he seems to have an apartment at pleasure in their house, and to love their children as if they were his own. He told us he had known Mrs. Dickinson from the time she was seven years old.'

In 1822 Strahan, giving evidence before a Select Committee, was able to say that he had been one of the greatest printers in

[1] C. Barrett, *Diary and Letters of Madame d'Arblay*, v, 1905, p. 421.
[2] A study of the elder Strahan is promised by Mr. Peter Cockayne, who has kindly given me information on the subject.

London for twenty or thirty years.[1] When young John was nearing his fifteenth birthday, on 7 February 1797, he was through Strahan's influence apprenticed to Thomas Harrison of Leadenhall Street, Stationer of London, for seven years, to learn his art,[2] perhaps with the idea of entering Strahan's business. On 6 March 1804 young Dickinson took up his freedom and was admitted to the livery of the Stationers' Company.

Three years before this John Dickinson had gone into business on his own account. A notebook of 1801[3] shows him making money by discounting bills, doubtless with Andrew Strahan to back him. By 1802 he was making a respectable income in this way, with George Stafford the paper-maker and various publishing firms, Rivington's among many others, as clients. By 1804 he was trading as a stationer in the City, at 2 Walbrook. His accounts show him in receipt of payments for paper from the proprietors of the *Gentleman's Magazine*, from publishers such as Rivington's, Eyre and Strahan's, Cadell's, Longman's, and Nichols's, and from booksellers such as Dulau's and Hatchard's. He did reasonably well, and at the end of his first year of business bought his mother a fine French watch to celebrate his success and express his gratitude.[4] For himself he bought a lottery ticket for £19, but had no luck in the draw.

In the following year he moved to 39 Ludgate Street (now Ludgate Hill) and took as his apprentice Matthew Blackley, son of a shoemaker of that name living in Mare Street, Hackney.[5] He received considerable sums from Strahan; £2,000 on

[1] Select Committee on Printing and Stationery, 30 July 1822; Blue Book, p. 213.

[2] The indenture is in the possession of Mr. John Dickinson Evans: the documents he has kindly lent me will be indicated in the footnotes by the letters J.D.E.

[3] In the possession of the Firm. When no provenance is given for a document, it may be inferred that it is in their archives.

[4] Now in the possession of John Dickinson Evans.

[5] J.D.E.

2 December 1805 and £6,000 in April 1806. These were clearly gifts or loans and in another category from the lesser sums paid by Strahan's firm for paper used in editions of the Bible, the Statutes and so on.

John Dickinson's parents knew many dignitaries of the East India Company. In 1803 they had moved from the Tower to a delightful house called Bramblebury at Woolwich, and there, and at Plumstead and Blackheath, they visited and dined at any number of fine houses where 'the Nabobs' lived. Their second son, Thomas Dickinson, entered the East India Company's service, in which he was to rise to the rank of Major-General; and by 1806 John Dickinson was supplying the East India Company with paper on a considerable scale. In that year he received from them nearly £3,200 in November, and over £2,800 the following April. The paternal connexion with the Board of Ordnance is reflected in a sale of nearly £1,100 to the Board in June.

So far John Dickinson had traded as a middle-man, selling paper made by others. The craft of paper-making had in England become one of the crafts, like distilling and the working of silver, that were traditionally in the hands of the descendants of Huguenot refugees;[1] indeed, letters patent of 1686 had given the Huguenots the monopoly of the white paper trade for fourteen years. Changing conditions in France had induced many French workmen to return to that country in the course of the eighteenth century, but the little world of Frances Dickinson's Huguenot friends and acquaintances must have included some of the Portals, Fourdriniers, and others, who continued in the trade.

The craft of paper-making had changed remarkably little

[1] See G. H. Overend, 'Notes upon the earlier History of Paper in England', in *Proceedings of the Huguenot Society of London*, VIII, 1905–8, p. 177. The Charter of the Stationers' Company dates from 1557; see S. Hodgson, *The Worshipful Company of Stationers*, 1953.

since the first English mill had been set up at Hertford by John Tate in 1490. It still consisted in the essential processes of reducing rags to fibre by boiling with a weak alkaline solution, bleaching the resultant pulp and then depositing it and felting it together on wire cloth while suspended in water.

The *English Encyclopedia* of 1802 describes the processes of sorting, picking, washing and breaking rags, and of new and partly mechanical methods of removing dust from them, and proceeds to a description of paper-making. The pulp was first prepared in the vat. The vatman used a hand mould, a fine wire sieve or wire cloth in a wooden frame. The wire part was slightly larger than the sheet of paper to be made, the actual limits of the sheet being determined by a movable and well-fitting raised-edge frame, known as the deckel or deckle, which has given its name to the raw uncut edge of the paper. Attached to or woven into the wire was a device whose purpose was to produce, by thinning the substance of the paper, the watermark—an ornament visible against the light, from whose design the traditional names of sizes of papers, such as crown, pott, foolscap, etc., were originally derived; or the maker's name; or a date; perhaps all three.

The vatman dipped his mould into the vat, brought it out horizontally and gave it a peculiar shake to 'lay' the rag fibres evenly. His assistant—the coucher—took the mould, let it drain and then turned it over, the paper falling upon a piece of felt. Felt and paper alternately were made into a pile, heavily pressed, the paper sheets removed from the felts and piled together, lightly pressed, and then separated and hung up on horsehair lines to dry. They were then dipped in a tub of size and again dried and pressed, following which came pressing, glazing or some other finishing process. With this technique paper could only be fabricated sheet by sheet, in sizes that could not exceed those of a frame that could be held and shaken by hand.

The years just after 1800 were years when the stress of war

and the threat of blockade stimulated invention. In 1802 a mechanical agitator, or 'hog', to agitate the fibre in the vat, was in use in England;[1] and in 1805[2] Joseph Bramah took out a patent for filling paper moulds of the old-fashioned kind by mechanical means, and for making paper in endless sheets on a wheel, by a method that clearly proved impracticable.

Meanwhile the idea of more fundamental innovations was in the air. As early as 1797 Nicolas Louis Robert,[3] a frail and sickly Frenchman who had already had to spend nine years in the French Army, was making a small model for the mechanical manufacture of paper on an endless web. When he had got out of the army in 1789 he had gone as a clerk to Saint-Léger Didot, a well-known Paris printer and publisher. After a few years he had shifted to paper-making in the mills of his employer's kinsman at Essonnes. Robert was a man of sensitive and difficult temperament, whom not even nine years in the army had turned into a good mixer; and the quarrelling and lack of discipline among the workers at Essonnes offended him. He envisaged, as an escape from such conditions, a paper-mill in which a machine would do the vatmen's work, and by producing lengths of paper instead of single sheets would simplify the labour and reduce the number of dry-workers.

It was an extraordinary incentive, but it led him to invent the first practicable paper machine: a machine which with many modifications is still in standard use. The first small model was made with Didot's encouragement in 1797; it did not work. Didot then took Robert out of the bustle of the Essonnes paper-mill into the comparative calm of a neighbouring flour-mill, where he could work and think in peace. Six months later,

[1] Dard Hunter, *Papermaking; the History and Technique of an Ancient Craft*, London, second edition, 1947, p. 525. Earlier experiments in the field had been made by Robert Cameron at Springfield Mills, near Edinburgh.

[2] Patent, 15 April 1805, No. 2840.

[3] On him see Dard Hunter, p. 341–73.

Didot provided Robert with technical assistants, and with their aid he produced an improved model. It still did not work. Didot insisted on Robert's continuing his experiments on a larger scale and at last, in 1798, a machine was produced that formed paper of the width of the machine on an endless wire-woven cloth, which drained away the superfluous water through the mesh. The paper was taken off in lengths while wet and was hung up to dry like hand-made paper.

A patent was secured in Paris on 18 January 1799, with the encouragement of the French Board of Trade. Soon after, Robert quarrelled with Didot, and refused to work with him further. He sold him his patent for 25,000 francs, to be paid in instalments. There was trouble over the payments, and in June 1801 Robert took back his patent.[1]

Meanwhile Didot, in 1799, had written to his brother-in-law, John Gamble, an English paper manufacturer, proposing that he should raise money in England to make a large machine on the lines of Robert's invention. Gamble succeeded in interesting two London stationers, Henry and Sealy Fourdrinier, in the scheme, and in 1803 the engineer Bryan Donkin made the machine, after additional patents had been secured.[2] The first machine made only a travesty of paper, but a second, erected at Frogmore Mills near Hemel Hempstead at the end of 1803, proved more successful. It was planned on a system of two wire sheets four feet wide and twenty-seven feet long, one over and one under the paper, but in 1805 Donkin changed it to work on the lower web only. A second, five foot, machine was set up the next year at Two Waters. By the time they had done, the Fourdriniers had spent some £60,000 upon the machine; but

---

[1] In 1801 Perrier adapted Robert's idea, including a couch roll.

[2] The first patent was granted on 20 April 1801, No. 2487; the second on 7 June 1803, No. 2708; and that for the continuous paper machine on 24 July 1806, No. 2951.

it worked.[1] In Donkin's final version the paper pulp was poured upon the horizontal portion of an endless web of woven wire which was constantly moving forward. A shaking motion, in imitation of the movements given to the mould by the vatman when making paper by hand, was imparted to the wire, and after much of the water had drained away and the newly formed film of paper had been partly consolidated, the paper web was pressed between a pair of rollers, one over and the other under the paper on the wire web. The paper was then separated from the wire and wound on a reel before being carried away to be unwound and hung up to dry. In 1807 a Private Bill was passed in Parliament to extend the Fourdriniers' patents for a further fifteen years.[2] Litigation followed, and by 1810 they were bankrupt.

Some time before this John Dickinson had embarked on experiments in making a rival machine. His account books show that he bought paper from the Fourdriniers in 1805,[3] though there is nothing to indicate whether it was hand-made paper from their mill in Kent or machine-made from their mill in Hertfordshire. In any case he must, as an intelligent and progressive stationer, have known of their experiments.

His account books from 1802 onwards show considerable and continuous payments to George Dodd, a well-known engineer

[1] See J. Strachan, 'The Evolution of the Fourdrinier Paper Machine' in supplement to *The Paper Maker and British Paper Trade Journal*, 1 May 1931, p. cxlii, and V. Sanguinetti in *World's Paper Trade Review*, 13 March 1931, p. 928.

[2] 14 August 1807, patent No. 3068*. Bryan Donkin (who had set up in Bermondsey as a manufacturer of paper-making machinery) was offering, in 1807, to build 30-inch machines, 3 or 4 vats, at from £715 to £750, and up to 54-inch machines, 12 vats, at from £995 to £1,040. The machines 'are durable. That at Two Waters for the last three years has not cost £10 a year in repairs.' Labour costs were stated to be 3/9 per cwt. against 16/– for hand-made paper.

[3] On 16 January 1805, Fourdriniers were paid £20 19s. od.; in May, £11 2s. 6d.

of the time, that suggest that he was having experimental machinery made to his own specifications.[1] The first outcome of these experiments was a patent, taken out on 30 June 1807,[2] for machinery for cutting and 'placing' paper made on the reels of the Fourdrinier machine. In Dickinson's design a grooved roller revolves at high speed; above it is a spindle carrying circular knives corresponding with the grooves in the roller beneath. As the paper unwinds from the reel and is drawn between the roller and the knives, it is cut longitudinally to the desired width or widths, and then, held between rods or parallel bars attached to revolving endless chains, it passes to the transverse cutting apparatus. Here two metal bars under the paper and two other bars above it clip the paper between them and cause a knife to cut the paper across its length. According to part of a later patent (1809),[3] a high-speed revolving circular knife-edge cutter acts transversely on the paper which, at the time of cutting, is supported by a grooved bar; tongs bite the paper and move it forward as required.

A second patent of this year—presumably a side-line, but one profitable to his country—was the patent Dickinson took out on 12 November 1807[4] for 'a cannon cartridge paper manufactured on an improved principle', by mixing in certain proportions wool or woollen rags to the linen rags or other material at the half-stuff stage, by means of which 'when the paper is lighted by the explosion of the powder in the gun, it is prevented from retaining sparks of fire after the flame goes out'. This paper did not smoulder and so cause premature explosions. Through his father's influence it was adopted by the Board of Ordnance and proved its worth in the Peninsular Campaign and at Waterloo.

Dickinson's chief ambition, however, lay in the invention of

---

[1] In 1805 Dodd receives very frequent payments of £20 or so.
[2] Patent No. 3056.
[3] Patent No. 3191, 19 January 1809.
[4] Patent No. 3080.

a machine for the actual manufacture of paper. On 19 January
1809 he was able to patent[1] not only improvements to his cutting
machine but also certain machinery for the manufacture of paper
by a new method. 'By this process a perforated brass hollow
cylinder, with closed ends, having its surface particularly constructed, and covered by an endless and tightly-drawn web of
woven wire, is made to emerge from a trough covered with pulp,
too moist to be pressed. To get rid of the superfluous moisture
there is a trough inside the cylinder with a pipe connected with
a pair of double-acting pumps, placed in a cistern of water, so
that the pumps draw the air out of the cylinder and the pulp is
pressed by atmospheric pressure. The web is picked up by an
endless felt passing round a couching roller lying on the making
cylinder.' A rather fuller description of the Dickinson machine[2]
makes its working clearer. It explains that he:

'makes use of a hollow brass cylinder or barrel closed at the
ends, but having a large hollow tube for the axis. This cylinder
is so contrived that the periphery of it is uniformly pervious to
water, and covered with fine woven wire. It is made to revolve
in a vat of very diluted pulp, in which it is about two-thirds
immersed: during the revolution of the cylinder the water
of the pulp passes through the pervious surface into the interior, and flows out through the hollow tube before mentioned,
each end of which passes through the sides of the vat in which
the cylinder revolves.

'As the water of the pulp flows through the surface of the
cylinder the fibres of rag floating in the vat are deposited on the
wire, and thereby gradually form the paper on every part of the
cylinder during its immersion in the fluid pulp. An endless felt

---

[1] Patent No. 3191. Further patents for improvements were taken
out in 1811 (No. 3452) (by which the paper was taken off the cylinder
not on to a brass roller but on to a cloth-covered one), 1814 (No. 3839),
1829 (No. 5754) and 1830 (No. 6008). The English patents did not
cover the United States, and by 1817 a plagiary of the Dickinson
cylinder machine was set up at the Gilpin paper-mill on the Brandy-
wine, near Wilmington, Delaware. Dard Hunter, p. 351.

[2] *London Encyclopedia*, 1829.

takes the paper off the highest point of the cylinder, with which it is brought in contact by the pressure of a roller, called technically the couching roll. The hollow axis before mentioned does not revolve with the cylinder, but is firmly fixed to the sides of the vat of pulp, through which it conveys the water from the interior of the cylinder, and it has attached to it troughs and other apparatus in the interior of the cylinder from which it is the channel of communication to two double acting air pumps, by the working of which two distinct effects are produced, both of which are essential to the operation of the machine. In the first place by drawing air from the inside of the cylinder a partial exhaustion of the interior is produced, and the influx of the water and the adhesion of the rag to the surface are promoted; in the next place the air so drawn away is forced into a receiver, where it is condensed, and from which it returns by a separate pipe to a long narrow trough in the inside of the cylinder parallel with the hollow axis, and under the place where the paper quits the cylinder and becomes attached to the endless felt which carries it away in a continued stream, the adhesion of this felt being produced by a continued blast of compressed air issuing from this trough, and which detaches the paper from the surface of the hollow cylinder on which it is made. The formation of the cylinder is very elaborate, and the apparatus essential to the process so complicated that the machine has not been adopted by any manufacturer except the original inventor Mr. Dickinson: but in his management it works with great precision and effect, and produces paper of very good quality.'

The advantages of the Dickinson machine over the contemporary Fourdrinier machine lay in the comparatively small degree of wire-mark in the paper, which resulted in a close approximation between the surface qualities of the two faces; and in the satin-like character that resulted from a large proportion of the fibres being laid in the direction in which the cylinder revolved.

John Dickinson is said to have erected and worked his trial machine on the roof of Andrew Strahan's office in Printer Street, where Strahan traded as King's Printer. It was evident that if he were to exploit the invention he must have his own mill.

It was natural enough that his eyes should turn to Hertford-shire, the county where the first English paper-mill had been set up just three centuries before. Many of its ancient flour-mills had been transformed into paper-mills; by 1800 there were eighteen paper-mills in the county. Fourdrinier's mills at Frogmore and Two Waters had drawn skilled men into the Hemel Hempstead area, and the increasing difficulties which these mills were experiencing were beginning to throw such workers upon the labour market. The neighbourhood was familiar to Dickinson; his sister, Harriet Dickinson, had married the Rev. John Septimus Grover, Vice-Provost of Eton, and the Vice-Provost's brother, Harry Grover, was the leading solicitor and banker in Hemel Hempstead.

Dickinson was accustomed to buying paper from George Stafford of Apsley Mill, Hemel Hempstead, and in May 1809 he acquired his mill. It was of very ancient origin as a flour-mill, being almost certainly one of the two mills in the parish of Abbots Langley mentioned in Domesday. It had remained a corn-mill belonging to the Abbey of St. Albans all through the Middle Ages[1] and later, but in the late eighteenth century had been converted to paper-making. The site of the mill had become more important when the Grand Junction Canal was opened in 1800, for the canal ran beside the mill and provided a highway for merchandise all the way to London.

Dickinson, who had as yet little capital of his own, acquired a partner in George Longman,[2] a man five years older than himself. He was the son of Thomas Longman, the second publisher of the name, and brother of the Thomas Norton Longman who was the current head of the publishing house. He was M.P. for Maidstone from 1806 to 1820, and we may suppose that his

[1] When the new Envelope Building was built in 1927 mediaeval walls were found in digging the foundations.
[2] He may have been a family friend; John Dickinson's mother's will mentions a vase of Derbyshire spar as having been given to her by him.

interest in the business was mainly financial. As the older and richer man, he was the senior partner, and the firm traded as Longman and Dickinson. It was in their joint names that the lease of 63 Old Bailey (later renumbered 65) was acquired on 22 March 1809, to serve as the London offices of the firm. At the same time they borrowed a considerable sum from Andrew Strahan; later receipts indicate that the interest on it amounted to over £2,000 a year.[1]

Even with such backing it must have taken courage to set up a new kind of manufacture in 1809. The idea of machine-made paper was still new, and its production still insignificant. In 1805[2] the 760 vats at work in the United Kingdom had produced 16,502 tons of paper, and the six paper machines only 557 tons. These machines were still entirely dependent on water power. It was only about 1800 that the improvements of Boulton and Paul had made the steam engine, invented a century earlier, available for ordinary mill purposes. Even so, with the available mechanisms, each horse power required 120 lb. weight of steam.

The Industrial Revolution was well under way, yet John Dickinson's patent for his paper-making machine[3] had still to be enrolled in the Chapel of the Rolls and to be inscribed by a clerk in an archaic Chancery hand on an immensely long roll of many membranes of parchment sewn together, with little to show where his patent ended and the next man's began, and the drawings sewn to flap at the side.

The year in which John Dickinson acquired Apsley Mill witnessed French victories in Spain, the successful negotiation by the victors of the Treaty of Vienna and the failure of the

[1] A letter from Dickinson to Strahan of 22 February 1809 is on the question of income tax on rent charge. Receipts of 9 July 1819, 6 January 1820 and 3 July 1820 are for £1,215 for half a year's rent charge on the Apsley Mill Estate.

[2] Dard Hunter, p. 526.

[3] The original is in the Public Record Office, Specification and Surrender Rolls, C.73 Part 27 No. 9 Membrane 12.

English expedition to Walcheren. His kinsman John Nash wrote to John Dickinson's mother[1] in that year: 'A crisis is at hand that will soon bring into action whatever power [the Government] possess—and from their measures we shall know the men. Here is peace and war huddled together—the levy en masse— the Volunteer system and regular force—reform and ancient establishment and toleration—Slave Trade and Catholic emancipation—all with their various opponents "cheek by jowl". Who will rise paramount and prevail we shall find out—if not (which I hope) that these various and heterogeneous materials may be thrown into the political alembic and an extract drawn from them more salutary for the body politic than were they administered crudely and unqualified.'

None the less Dickinson threw all he had, and a great deal that he had borrowed, into the acquisition of Apsley Mill in 1809: a hazardous venture, that only good fortune and hard work could bring to fruition.

[1] J.D.E.

II

APSLEY AND NASH MILLS
1809–1823

JOHN DICKINSON lived at first in the little mill-house at Apsley. He naturally saw a good deal of his connexions, the Grovers, both at the bank owned by Harry Grover and James Pollard and at the hospitable house of The Bury, Hemel Hempstead. It was indeed a family house: Harry Grover was one of a family of ten sons and his wife Sibylla Ehret[1] of another of ten daughters and a son: and they themselves had fifteen children, of whom fourteen lived to grow up.

In 1810 John Dickinson proposed for the hand of the second of these, Ann, and shortly afterwards married her. She was a gay and pretty creature in those days, full of energy, and clearly a good wife for a young manufacturer, in her own right as well as in that of a banker's daughter.

It is not always remembered that the Industrial Revolution could hardly have been effected without the aid of the country bankers, whose business, like that of the factories, increased and multiplied during the Napoleonic Wars.[2] They extended the

[1] She was the daughter of George Dionysius Ehret, F.R.S., a man who had risen from being a gardener at Erfurt to become the most eminent botanical painter in Europe. His autobiography will be found in the *Proceedings of the Linnaean Society of London*, November 1894 to June 1895, p. 41.

[2] L. S. Pressnell, 'Public Monies and the Development of English Banking', in *Economic History Review*, 2nd series, v, 1953, p. 378, states that there were a bare handful of such banks in England and Wales in 1750; about 120 by 1784; some 300 in the early 1790's; almost 400 by 1801 and not far short of 800 in the peak year of 1810.

traditional country solicitors' business of mortgages on land and houses to advances on factories, built and unbuilt, and on the profits of manufactures as yet unmade. It was a risky business, but without their acceptance of the risk many manufactures could have been neither begun nor developed. It is certain that John Dickinson's venture owed a great deal to the support of Grover's Bank.[1]

A few months after his marriage John Dickinson bought Nash Mills, about half a mile down stream from Apsley, a paper-mill that had the added advantage of a good modern mill-house and a pleasant garden. It was as old, as a corn-mill, as Apsley, and like it had been recorded in Domesday, and like it had belonged in the Middle Ages to the Abbey of St. Albans.[2] It had been converted to paper by A. Blackwell towards the end of the eighteenth century;[3] Dickinson bought it from him and his partner G. Jones.

The Mill House was a stuccoed house that turned two faces to the world. On the Mill side to the north, where John Dickinson's library window overlooked all the comings and goings of the office and the works, it showed a rather dreary face; but on the south it presented a not inelegant pedimented façade, with the long windows of the drawing- and dining-rooms, a pillared porch up a flight of steps, and a long orangery leading out on to the smooth lawns that the Mill boatmen used to scythe between voyages.

[1] The Bank is now represented by the Hemel Hempstead Branch of Lloyds Bank; the Manager, Mr. J. R. Turnbull, is researching into its history.

[2] A document of 1355 mentions 'Assemille'; the abbot had trouble over the repair and rent of the mill, which was farmed out to John de Chilterne. There seems a possibility that it was at one time a fulling-mill for cloth.

[3] The Mill still possesses a number of old hand-moulds, with the following names or initials: A. Blackwell, 1798; A. Blackwell and Jones, 1802; G. Stafford, 1804; K.G., 1805; and G. Jones every year from 1804 to 1810. The first mould with Dickinson's name is dated 1811.

The Dickinsons started their married life at Nash House under reasonably happy auspices. Ann loved her husband, though she was afraid of his temper. Too often she had to make such entries in her journal[1] as:[2] 'Quarrel'd with my dr. Husband for his harsh language to me, said more than I ought, and as usual repented it.' His temper, indeed, and still more his capacity for strong language, became a legend that is still remembered in the valley of the Gade. One who himself just remembered him,[3] and knew many who had known him well, recorded: 'He seems to have been able to swear at everything and everybody, and on any occasion, and when he was in a bad temper (which he often was) his ability in this direction was apparently greater . . .' He was extremely hot tempered, and when he was in this state it was said by someone who knew him that 'he kicked like a serpent and threw his legs about like a 90-gun ship'.

In spite of their difficulties he had a considerable respect for his wife's ability. It was perhaps the Huguenot tradition that women had good minds for business that made him accept her as a confidante in his affairs. He showed her all his improvements, and let her help with the accounts; and when he had to go to London for the day she would usually walk round both Mills to see that things were going well. The family nature of the business is well attested by an entry of 3 February 1821: 'Mr. D. began to size my Father's new Bank Notes and on opening them found they were so irregularly put up that they must all be counted and sorted . . . I went up to Apsley and assisted Mr. D. with the wages. After tea I dictated them and he copied them into the Ledger.'

[1] I am greatly indebted to my cousin, Mrs. Lowry Cole, for lending me the MS. diaries of Ann Dickinson and her daughter Fanny, later Mrs. Pratt Barlow. They are now in the library of Bedford College, University of London.

[2] 28 April 1822.

[3] His great-nephew Lewis Evans, at a lecture at Croxley given on 5 March 1897.

Ann Dickinson was a notable housewife, baking her bread at home, making her own butter and supervising the concoction of jams and jellies and pickles in the still-room, even when she had a footman to answer the door and a nurse to tend the babies, as well as cooks and housemaids.

The tragedy of their wedded life lay in the deaths of their young children. Ann bore a son, John Moody Dickinson, in 1811; he died in 1812. John Henry, born in 1812, died in 1813. Samuel, born in 1820, died in 1826; William, born in 1821, died in 1832. Only John, born in 1815, and two daughters—Frances Elizabeth, born in 1814, and Harriet Ann, born in 1823—survived. The sad truth is that those who died were the victims of Ann's sense of duty and of her belief in the medical lore of the day. However young they were, and whatever was wrong with them—a cold in the head, a liver chill, a headache, a fit of bad temper, a feverish attack, a broken collar-bone—she conscientiously dosed them with calomel; if there was nothing wrong she gave a precautionary dose every few days. Calomel is a cumulative poison, and few survived.

The Grover relationship with many of the local landed families—Days of Sarratt, Finches of Redheath, Moodys of Carpender's, Pearses and Dysons of Watford, Ways of Denham—brought the Dickinsons into the hospitable society of West Hertfordshire, and they in due course returned the hospitality. In June 1828, for example, they gave 'a little evening party . . . 53 people almost all relations'. When they gave a dinner party nearly all the food was home-grown: beef, mutton, pork, poultry and eggs all came from the little farm that lay between Nash Mills and the village. When the mill-stream was drawn and the water was low great catches of fish were made—on 7 May 1822, '7½ brace of trout, of between 3 and 4 lbs. each, and 284 different sized jack from 5 to 1½ lbs. each, besides bushells of small ones, and very large roach and dace'—which, with eels from Batchworth, usually provided a fish course; at other times

Mr. Wise, the clerk at the firm's offices in the Old Bailey, would send down sea-fish by the coach from London, which had to be met at the Red Lion. The Dickinsons received a good many presents of game from the neighbouring estates, and used to send trout and eels in return. They gathered quantities of fruit from the young trees in Nash Mills garden, and a prolific pear orchard behind the Mill at Apsley. The scale of Ann's hospitality may be judged by the hamper she sent in May 1822 to her little daughter at school: '3 couple Chickens, 250 Asparagus, 2 doz. Cabbages, bunch radishes, bunch Mint, bundle rhubarb, jar of Blk. currant jelly, do. Strawberry Jam and a large nosegay. Sent by boat.'

Dickinson, who was a good horseman, found time to hunt with the Old Berkeley. On 20 March 1824 Ann writes: 'Dearest much knock'd up, he was in at the death and was hunting and on horseback for 5 hours.'

Ann Dickinson did not get on with her masterful mother-in-law; when she came to Nash Mills the old lady used to spend most of her time in conclave with her son, going over accounts. Otherwise they saw little of his own family. John's most successful brother was in India, and his favourite sister was married to a wine-grower, Joseph Phelps, in Madeira; he saw little of the two sisters who had married clergymen, the Rev. J. S. Grover and the Rev. A. B. Evans.

Though Ann Dickinson was thus little troubled by entertaining her husband's relations, she had frequently to play her part as hostess to his business acquaintances, who often came for a weekend. In 1822, for instance, Monsieur and Madame Didot came from Friday to Monday.[1] On Friday evening Ann records: 'They do not speak a word of English. Did not get on well at first. Was very tired at night.' By Sunday things were going better. 'Like the French people very much—They are very pressing for me and my children to go and see them in

[1] 29 March–1 April. Didot came to Nash Mills again in 1829.

Paris. None of us went to church.' Three weeks later 'a French gent. a considerable Paper Maker near Lyons named Gançon came down by coach to see the Mills and dined here'. In July 'Mr. D. came down with a Mr. Tennant from Glasgow an eminent pratical [*sic*] Chymist, a very pleasant man'. He was followed by Koenig and Bauer, the inventors of the cylinder printing-press[1] that exploited machine-made paper in rolls. Again on 19 September 1823 Ann Dickinson records in her diary: 'Mr. D. came down and brought Mr. Koenig a very clever man and a mechanist.' In August 1824 the Constables came to stay on their way to Scotland; in July 1825, Blackwood 'The Edinburgh bookseller'; and in September Brunel the engineer, the Murrays, and the d'Israelis came to lunch and to see the Mills.

The Mills, indeed, were beginning to be one of the sights to be seen by visitors to Hertfordshire. In August 1813 Joseph Farington, the diarist, was staying with Davies the publisher at Rickmansworth. On the 16th he 'went with Mr. and Mrs. Davis to Dickinson's paper Mills abt. 7 miles from Rickmansworth, and was highly gratified on seeing the process of making paper as it is now carried on . . . Davis told me that their House (Cadell and Davis) pay to Dickinson £12,000 pr. annum for paper . . .'

It would seem probable that Mr. Davies considerably exaggerated this total, in order to impress his distinguished guest; there is no evidence of Longman and Dickinson's trading with him on anything approaching this scale. None the less, business was satisfactory. In 1812 Samuel Bagster had embarked on the

---

[1] In 1811 Frederick Koenig invented and constructed a cylinder printing-press, and in 1813 he and his partner Bauer got it into production. In the following year they furnished two presses to *The Times*. The first newspaper to be printed on a cylinder press was the issue of *The Times* of 29 November 1814, printed with the aid of papier-mâché matrices.

publication of his *Pocket Reference Bible,* and John Dickinson had succeeded in producing a thin, tough and opaque paper which exactly met his requirements for it. The New Testament was issued in 1812, and the Old in the following year; their immense success represented a great sale of paper from Apsley and Nash Mills. The Rev. T. F. Dibdin, in his *Bibliographical Decameron* of 1817 says: 'The firm of Longman Dickinson & Co. has recently improved even upon the excellent Didot's (Fourdrinier) machinery and has produced a sort of India-paper-tinted "article", quite delightful in colour, and apparently of equal excellence in substance. There is a story extant that a few of the principal London manufacturers of paper made a *bet* respecting the production of the finest "article" in the trade; and who should *win* this bet but the House of Longman Dickinson & Co.?! Mr. Dickinson, who more especially directs the concern, is a smart, lively, energetic little man; born for action, and full of eagerness and enthusiasm to shine in his business.'

In the months following Waterloo Dickinson had begun to trade overseas. A 'Second of Exchange' payable through Rabone Brothers, of Birmingham, shows that in December 1815, Downey and Eastburns, of New York, were paying the Dickinson firm £168 for goods supplied.

In 1819 Hassell, in his *Tour of the Grand Junction Canal,* says that Apsley Mill 'within a short period has been considerably enlarged, occupying a large space of ground and rather resembling a village than a manufactory'.

In that year the firm was supplying Constable's, the Clarendon Press, Whittaker's, Bensley's, Rivington's and Parker's of Oxford. In 1820 they supplied Eyre and Strahan, the King's Printers, with over £6,500 worth of paper for an edition of the Bible, and the University of Cambridge with nearly £1,050 worth of paper. On 1 July 1821 Ann Dickinson wrote in her diary: 'My dear Husband was made very happy by a fine order from Waddell for 1880 Rms. of fine foolscap the best order they ever had.' A further order for 5,000 reams followed in November 1822 and was important enough for Dickinson to write from London to tell his wife of it.

The scale of the Mills' production can be guessed at by a certificate of 12 July 1816 to say that 1,712 lb. of salt, duty free, had been used to make bleach at the Mills in the presence of an excise clerk between 3 July and 3 August 1815. In 1818 Dickinson took over a small paper-mill at Batchworth[1] and developed it for the production of half-stuff. He installed new machines there[2] and had some trouble with them; Telford the engineer came to see them in December.[3]

None the less John Dickinson had his set-backs in these early years. On 26 October 1813 there was a bad fire at Nash Mills. Nearly all the Mill was destroyed, though the machine-house was not damaged; the Dickinsons' own house was only saved from destruction by being hung with wet paper-felts. Dickinson himself was away in London. A messenger was sent to find him and wake him. His first cry on hearing the news was 'Thank God!' for he had feared that his wife, who was expecting a baby, had died.[4]

The damage done was between seven and eight thousand pounds, but was covered by insurance.[5] The redevelopment of the Mills that ensued was on two main lines. First, steam-power sufficient to work three machines was introduced at Apsley in 1815; and second, after the Fourdrinier machine had been developed on a successful commercial basis at Two Waters in 1812,[6]

[1] According to Ann's diary of 28 July, 'Batchworth was set to work for us Saturday 24th inst.'.

[2] Ann Dickinson's diary, 12 and 16 October 1818.

[3] *Ibid.*, 20 December.

[4] *Ibid.*

[5] In February 1821 Batchworth Mill had a narrow escape from a chimney fire which spread to bales of rags.

[6] Dard Hunter, p. 532.

Dickinson hired from H. Bloxam (the assignee of the estate of H. & S. Fourdrinier, in bankruptcy) two Fourdrinier machines for £100 a year.[1] By 1822 the wire webs on which both sorts of machines laid the wet paper were being woven at Apsley.[2]

The basis of Dickinson's business, even in 1815, was production on a large scale, yet by that year his raw materials—rags—were in short supply. He did not buy only on the London market, but, as soon as the peace that followed Waterloo permitted, traded directly with foreign rag merchants. In November 1816, for instance, he bought 220 bags of White Tuscan Rags from the firm of Reed, Bell & De Jongh of Leghorn, 'shipped for your account and risk per English Brig Cosmopolite, Captain Barber, on the point of sailing direct for London', at a cost of £789. The letter continues: 'The article of Tuscan Rags is very scarce here, owing to large shipments making to America and to Scotland; therefore, no reduction of price can be expected for the present. Indeed, we find the use, now so commonly made in this Country, of British Cotton Goods, influences to render Linen Rags scarce.'

It was a normal business hazard that his customers—notably Constable, whom the firm had to sue for £500 in 1820—were for ever demanding time to pay,[3] and a normal paper-making risk that he had trouble over his water-power. At Apsley and Nash the Grand Junction Canal and the River Gade, with its tributary the Bulbourne, ran side by side, and the canal was already being developed to steal some of the water from the rivers.

On 17 March 1818 an Act was passed to enable the Grand Junction Canal to vary the line of part of their waterway in this

[1] Receipts survive dated July 1814 and January 1817.
[2] Ann Dickinson's diary, 10 May 1822. A new wire-shop at Nash Mills was built in 1843; the manufacture continued there until about 1893.
[3] e.g. letters from Constable of 11 September 1817 and 28 July 1820.

region. Its preamble states that disputes have existed for several years between the Company and the owners of Nash and Apsley Mills over the subtraction of water from the Mills by the canal. The Act, by express agreement with Longman and Dickinson's, permits the canal between Frogmore Swing Bridge and its junction with the tail-water of Nash Mills to have a new course along the united Bulbourne and Gade. The Canal Company covenants not to make any alteration in the communication between the canal and the rivers north of Nash Mills otherwise than as authorized by the Act, nor to make any further diversion of any of the water in the rivers, and not to stop their canal boats near the garden of Nash Mill House.

On 14 March 1818 water fell for the first time over the new tumbling bay and on the 22nd Ann records: 'Mr. D. opened the Channel from Nash Mill head to new line of Canal.' In August a new line of canal at Batchworth was opened, and Dickinson dined with the Canal Committee afterwards.

Dickinson had contracted to carry out the brickwork for the new canal, and supervised it himself. He and a workman named Marks had a violent quarrel over where a marking-post should be set in the ground. They came to blows, and Dickinson was well and truly beaten in the fight. The next day the workman expected to get the sack; instead Dickinson gave him half a crown and later made him sub-foreman at Batchworth.

The new channels of water soon led to modifications in the machinery. On 3 May 1822 they 'sat up all night with the new wheel', and at Nash on the 20th the 'Mill head [was] drawn down, great wheel calk'd and a great deal doing'. On 22 November John and Ann walked up to Apsley and found such a head of water that all the machines had to be set to work. In April and May 1823 there was further trouble with the wheel, and Nash Mills stood still for eight weeks.

These were not the only troubles; the steam-engine proved as unreliable as the water-wheel. On 23 September the 'great

Steam Engine boiler burst', and when they came to examine the new one that was ready it was found faulty. On 9 February 1824 'in the middle of the night we were awoke by one of the men to say the overshot waterwheel was broken down. Dearest got up and was seeing the people and making arrangements for two hours.' It burst again on 18 October. 'Oh! what torments!', poor Ann wrote in her diary.

In spite of Acts of Parliament Dickinson was very conscious of the danger that lay in the Canal Company's claims on the water of his valley, and characteristically tried to meet it by getting himself appointed an officer of the Company. On 2 January 1821 his wife records: 'Mr. D. . . . sent his offer for the situation of Superintendent to Gd. Jn. Canal Co to Mr. Praed. God prosper him! January. 6 . . . My Father call'd to bring a letter from Ld. Bridgewater, too much against Mr. D.'s application to be pleasant . . .' Grover duly interviewed Lord Bridgewater on 12 January, and was able to bring back a favourable account of his conversation, but on 11 February he had to tell them that there was no chance of the appointment. 'My Father . . . told us the Superintendent situation is to be vested in the Select Committee so Mr. D.'s prospect has failed, a thing we neither of us much regret.'

In 1818 John Dickinson's mother, in return for a loan, had insisted on John's taking her youngest son George into the mill. He was an awkward, difficult, loutish youth, and a great trial to his sister-in-law and brother, with whom he lived at Nash House for some years after 1818. Ann, in particular, despised what she called 'his eye-service and lazy disposition'. On 19 January 1821 she records: 'Mr. D. had letter by coach, to say all the East India Ammun[itio]n was bad, so they will be obliged to take it back at a great loss, owing to Geo.'s not attending to it while they made it, a loss of 200£.' A week later, on 27 January, she writes: 'After dinner they came and told Mr. D.

that there were no Logwood chips[1] and in consequence the Mill and Machines had to wait 2 days, and my poor Husband was almost out of his wits he was so worried, it turn'd out too, that G[eorge] D[ickinson] knew they were not arrived and never took the trouble to stir about it.' Two days later she continues: 'My dear Husband much distressed to get the dry-work done owing to Geo.'s sending away our only two good hands.' On 1 February she writes: '. . . Walk'd up to Apsley . . . My dear Husband found in great agitation, having found that during his absence in town Geo. had spoilt the Ammun.[n] making for the East I. Cy. being the 2nd. parcel he has spoilt for this one order. Mr. D. was quite ill with the worry. The consequence is that not half the order can be sent up to-day and it has every prospect of being rejected, and they are obliged to make more of it.'

Trouble continued. On 23 March she writes: 'G.D. was very impertinent to my dr. Husband this morning on his saying that if some paper was not forwarded we shd. lose the East India business. What will be the upshot of this brutal conduct I cannot imagine but I am sure it is enough to drive him mad to have such a savage to deal with.'

Dickinson set about trying to get money from other sources, so as to release the capital that his mother had put into the business on his brother's account.[2] In October Andrew Strahan lent him £12,500, and negotiations continued, neither easily nor happily. On 3 August 1822 Ann wrote: 'Dr. Husband return'd by Mail knock'd up and unhappy and looking ill. Had a good deal of talk on the business now pending. Oh! that I had from the first set down every step of this proceeding! It wd. have been a memorial of meanness and tyranny seldom exhibited!'

[1] Logwood chips were used in the preparation of dyes, for paper as for other things. The revolutions against Spain in South America may well have made the supply uncertain.

[2] In July 1841 John Dickinson paid off a mortgage of £7,000 on Apsley Mills to Joseph Rawlings.

In August Dickinson went to his mother's to settle about George renting Buckland Mills, near Dover, to which he finally departed in December 1822.[1] In September a Mr. Rutt came over to see the Mills with a view to taking his place. In November George Longman, Dickinson's sleeping partner, died. His brother and executor objected to Mr. Rutt and he could not be engaged. Finally George Longman's nineteen-year-old nephew Charles was apprenticed to Dickinson in May 1823.[2] Philip Meadows Taylor, a man who had failed in business in Liverpool and Dublin, was appointed to supervise Apsley Mills when John Dickinson could not be there himself; Charles Longman in his turn spent most of his time at Batchworth. Young Longman lodged with the Taylors in a little house that Dickinson had built at Apsley.

John Dickinson could brook no competition to his authority and preferred to work with young men or paid subordinates. The changes, however, had reminded him that he did not in fact own the firm, and he was restless under the pricks. In July and August 1823 he even spent three weeks in Paris investigating the possibilities of taking a share in a French paper-making business recommended by Didot, but at length decided against it. On 30 December 1825 Ann was able to write in her diary: 'My dear husband . . . is about to change the name of his Firm and it is to be carried on in his name only for the future.'

John Dickinson had already faced his first labour troubles in 1821. The first Union in the trade, the Original Society of Papermakers, had been founded in 1800; the protest was made at their instance. The end of 1820 found trade falling and

---

[1] Ann records on 2 November 1822 their horror at his extravagance in buying a 10-horse steam-engine from Birmingham for the Mill and two machines before he had 'a certain vent for his paper'. George Dickinson died in 1843.

[2] In their turn the Strahan family seem to have objected to this. Diary, 10 May 1823.

Dickinson tried to reduce expenses. On 1 January 1821 Ann records: 'Mr. D. had a great deal of trouble with the Dye-workers and finishers, about lowering their wages, and it is not yet finish'd.' Five days later she wrote: 'All the Papermakers gave warning to-day and are to be off on Monday. Mr. D. is gone again up to Apsley this eveng. to look after them . . .' On the Monday all the malcontents were gone.

Dickinson at once set about filling their places. On 7 January Ann writes: 'Mr. D. was very much occupied all the Morning arranging new setts of workmen in place of those who have left . . . Mr. D. set on 4 Labourers as Engineers and was up all night to look after them. God prosper him! and enable him to turn his noble mind to religion and its peaceful paths, for the turmoil and fatigue of business is sorely against deep and fervent prayer.' She continues the next day: 'Mr. D. got to bed at 4 of this morng. Rose at 9. Had a number of men from A[bbots] L[angley] parish to select workmen from . . . Mr. D. gets on very well with his new hands, but seems fatigued and out of spirits. He grieves so very much for the families and wives of these infatuated men . . .' On the following day: 'Mr. D. hir'd some more Men. He sent notices to all the Men to quit their Cottages—some of the poor Wives much distressed . . .' Feeling evidently ran high. On 11 January '. . . They lost one of new Excise labels supposed to have been stolen for mischief.' Dickinson was beginning to weaken a little. On 20 January: 'Mr. D. sent and offer'd Wright his place again as Machine man, but he was fool enough to prefer going to his Parish with his 6 children rather than accept of 28/-s pr. wk. and his house rent.' On 14 February: 'Two officers from Excise came down to-day to search the premises in consequence of some of these villains who went away laying an information that they run the Duty. Nothing was found to confirm this assertion and they went back apparently satisfied but it is impossible to tell what may be the up-shot of such villainous dispositions.' Five days later: 'Mr. D.

told me somebody had got into Apsley Machine house and tried to spoil all the work by altering the parts of the machinery. Luckily no great mischief was done.'

Gradually things settled down; but the legend remained that 'John Dickinson could make a paper maker out of a hedge'. Poor Ann Dickinson wrote on 30 January in her diary: 'I had a kind letter from Miss Phelps asking us to go there next week to go to Drury Lane with them, I declined because it would mean expence my beloved Husband can ill afford for me and besides I can't bear pleasure while he is so unhappy.'

III

THE YEARS OF INVENTION
1817–1832

W HEN Philip Meadows Taylor, who knew nothing of
paper-making,[1] was installed as supervisor at Apsley in
1823, he was provided with a notebook to serve him
as a guide,[2] with everything in it he would need, from a list of
the chief employees in the Mills to a description of the processes
of manufacture and a glossary of technical terms. From the
list[3] it appears that at Apsley at this time the men employed
included two engine-men, each with an assistant; two men with
an assistant to look after the steam-engines, with four other men
under them; a picker, and a press-man who also carried half-stuff.
In the Machine House one man looked after the great machine
and another after two small machines; a third tended the steam
rolls with an assistant; and two acted as cutters. The dry-work
was carried out by four men and a boy, with two pressers. The
Salle had a foreman, six finishers, two pressers and a cutter of
dry paper; and there were two millwrights.

At Nash Mills there were four engine-men, with as many
assistants; two men and two assistants on the machines; a man
and his assistant for the steam rolls, and two cutters. There were

---

[1] His eldest son, of the same name, left for India soon after the
family came to Apsley, and made a name for himself. He acted as
The Times correspondent between 1840 and 1853, and wrote six
successful stories based on Indian history. See Colonel Meadows
Taylor, *The Story of My Life*, London, 1878. On his archaeological
work see Sir Mortimer Wheeler, *Archaeology from the Earth*, 1954, p. 8
et sqq.

[2] J.D.E.   [3] Appendix A.

30

three carpenters, under a foreman. The dry-work was done by two pressers, four men for sizing, four finishers and a cutter of dry paper.[1]

The women employees were evidently numerous, but are not listed. A contemporary account[2] describes their work in preparing the rags. 'In a long room, filled with dust, are some twenty or thirty women employed in sorting and cutting rags. Each woman stands at a frame, or table, whose top is covered with wire; on her left is a quantity of rags; on her right a box divided into three compartments. On a part of the table an upright knife, about a foot long, is fixed. This formidable instrument looks like the broken blade of a scythe, and we believe it is so. It is the business of the woman to sort and cut the rags. She spreads a few on the wire frame before which she stands, and as she shakes them a great deal of the dirt passes through the wire to a box beneath. If the pieces are small enough—and they are required not to be larger than three or four inches square— she throws each piece into one of the compartments of the box on her right, according to its quality. If a piece requires to be cut, she draws it across the blade of the knife, by which it is instantly divided. She is particularly careful to put all seams by themselves; for the sewing thread, if not thoroughly ground, would produce filaments in the paper. These operations are performed with great rapidity. An active workwoman can sort and cut about a hundred-weight a day. When cut and sorted the rags are weighed, and removed in bags containing each a hundred-weight.'

The women had their own homes to tend, and excellent reasons

---

[1] It is a remarkable instance of continuity that of the sixty-three surnames occurring in the list of 1823 (see Appendix A) thirty-five are still (1955) represented among the employees of the Mills. A few may be coincidental, but in a number of instances there is no doubt that the same family is represented.

[2] *Penny Magazine*, supplement, 31 August 1833.

for lateness or absence that usually had to be accepted. On the last day of 1824, however, Dickinson 'found women late to their work and made a great stir about it'. The next day (a Sunday) Ann tells us: 'Dearest has the women to work to-day owing to the small quantity of Paper got out this week.'

Meadows Taylor's notebook lays down no instructions for the hours of work; some of its calculations suggest that a twelve-hour day was worked. One entry states: 'Stuff enough should be got off to keep the Machines going 3 Nights in the Week.'

The notebook gives a clear account of how the work in the Mills was done. It appears to be in Taylor's own handwriting, but a good deal seems to have been dictated, and we hear Dickinson's own decisive voice behind the written words.

'The greatest nicety in paper making, the part of the process which requires the most constant attention and judgment, is the preparation of the pulp or *stuff* as it is technically called . . .

'Tender rags require *beating* with dull tackle—strong rags require *cutting* with sharp tackle. In proportion as the *stuff* parts with water freely, or the reverse, in the process of making it into paper, it is calld wet stuff or fast stuff . . .

'The greater number of bars in a roll or plate, the wetter the stuff will be supposing equal sharpness, because the number of surfaces prevent the chopping action . . . When stuff is hammered too much in the breaking in, it cannot be brought to a right temper afterwards, but is said to be greased. As the multiplicity of steel in the beater has a tendency to render stuff wet and as strong rags are liable to form wet stuff at any rate, it is the practice to grind them a good deal in the washer before letting them down in the beater. This is called *shortening the stuff in the washer*. It is always desirable to avoid this, and it is only resorted to for the purpose of properly tempering the stuff . . .

'The other grand distinction in stuff is in respect of the length of the Fibre which depends on the process of Grinding . . . For strength, it is desirable to have the Fibres long—for beauty it is desirable to have them short. Our rule is to have the Stuff as long as will allow of the paper looking tolerably well thro'.

'Bleaching . . . is performed at Batchworth Mill upon the half stuff. It has no weakening effect upon the Rags unless they lie a considerable length of time after it without the *gas* being washed out. It is desirable therefore to arrange for the supply so as to have no great deposits of bleached stuff at any time.

'The greater part of the Rag used at Apsley and Nash Mills arrives in the state of Half Stuff. It is then put into the washing engines and the Gas washed out for about an Hour. If the colour and quality require to be heightened, it is then further bleached by the admixture of bleaching Liquid to the stuff in the Engine which after running an hour is washed out. This operation is called *Salting*. Before the stuff is let down into the beating engine it is commonly a little more ground, called *shortening*, but this process should always be avoided if possible as it occasions waste.

'When the stuff is brought to the requisite quality, that it has nothing to undergo but compleating the grinding process, it is let down into the beating Engine. When there, the Roll is let down upon the plate and the grinding continued till it is brought to the requisite degree of fineness or *shortness* of Fibre. The roll is then a little tightened up (for about $\frac{1}{4}$ of an Hour) and the stuff is what is called *cleared* and . . . let into the Chest or receptacle for stuff and kept mixed . . .

'The Machine goes faster or slower according to the thickness of the Paper and the wetness of the stuff.

'It is desirable to have the stuff as wet as possible consistently with the paper running round without cockling. The rate of the Machine going for most descriptions of paper is accurately ascertained. If at the prescribed rate of going the Water does not disappear at the usual point that is an indication of the Stuff being too wet and the paper so made will come round cockly. The Engineers (that is the Men who look after the Engines[1]) are always to blame when that is the case. The responsability ought to rest with them of getting the stuff the right temper, unless they complain of their Tackle, and are told to keep on as they are . . .

'For *printing* it is better to have paper sized in the Engine. For *Writing* and *Drawing* it is sized in the Tub. *Copperplate* papers have *no size*.

[1] i.e. the beater-engine.

'In Engine sizing, the Ingredients are mixed with the stuff in the Engine, and beat with it . . . We use 3 lb. Alum, ¾ lb soap boiled with water, and a little plaister of paris. If the paper is wanted to bear very strongly, we use larger proportions of the two former articles. Rapid drying is very much against the bearing of the Paper, whether it be Tub sized, or Engine sized . . .

'Size for sizing in the Tub is made by boiling parchment pieces or Scrolls or size pieces as they are sometimes called. A given Quantity is put into a large Copper, and it requires 3 times boiling to extract all the Gelatine from them . . . In Letting out of the Copper the size is made to pass through *pounded Alum*, by which means a good deal is dissolved, and carried into the size.

'*Alum* is essential to make the paper bear, and prevent the size from becoming mouldy, but should not be in excess, as it renders the surface rough, and sometimes after the paper's being wetted, chrystalizes afresh on the surface.

'The paper is dipt in, in handfuls, in the operation of sizing, and kept in, till it is well soaked. It is then pressed to get rid of the superfluous size, and parted, and laid afresh, sheet by sheet, after which it must stand to get cold before it is hung on the Lines to dry. Fast stuff soaks most freely, but parts with the size again. Wet stuff soaks with difficulty, and in pressing is apt to stick together, and to tear in parting, which is technically called *peeling*.

'The size is more or less diluted according as the paper soaks. Free stuff will absorb strong size. Wet stuff will not perhaps soak in it at all . . . Hot size enters most freely but the paper does not bear so well, as when it is used colder. Hambro'[1] Rags, are not to be depended upon for holding size. Italian Rags are much worse: they will absorb size made twice as strong, as for English paper, and feel firm, but will not bear writing . . .

'The hanging the paper to dry, and pulling it down again, is called dry Work. The paper hangs on hair Lines, called simply *Lines*. The Lines require to be tight, and the moveable wooden bars to which they are attached, are called Trebles . . . The dry worker lays his pack on a small Table called a stool, and he takes

---

[1] i.e. rags from Hamburg.

up 4 or 5 sheets together, and hangs that Quantity across the Line, which is called a Spur . . .

'In the dry work, the thing to guard against is their taking up too thick Spurs, which occasions the paper to crease in the back, and if the paper is Tub-sized, is more likely to occasion it to mildew . . .

'The women receive the paper from the dry-workers, and are paid so much per Ream for their Work. They take 2 or 3 Reams together, and as the Paper cannot in that state be counted it is weighed to them , as it is intended to come round when finished. The *separating* the sheets is called *stripping*. The scratching off the Knots etc. is called picking. *Sheets* with any defects are separated and subsequently overlooked. All sheets thrown out in their way are called *sorts* . . .

'After picking it is the business of the Women to jog up their paper and deliver it to the finisher, with the Edges even. The *sorts* as they are called being on the top of the Heap which is called a *Wad*. These are put into the press, and a press-full is termed a Press of Wads. The inspector takes the paper out of the Press, puts aside the Sorts and turns over the Paper, rejecting any that is *cockly*, and returning to the Women any that are improperly picked. The paper is then Jogged again, and put into the press to be pressed *in the flat*, and after pressing it is said to be ready for *letting out*. Where a very good surface is required the Jogging and pressing are repeated. The paper is then counted out (called letting out) folded and put into the Press again in Reams, in which state it is called a Press of Reams.

'If made from Steam Engine size good papers (scalded) to be got off regularly.[1] If prepared at the old Mill scalded papers to be added regularly to each Engine . . .

'In starting on a fresh paper see that the Apron leather lays well and no rolls made, also try the deckle straps frequently, that they may not injure the wire by being too tight down. Always see that the paper is not moved at the Wet press, or water marked from fine wet stuff.

'Never suffer an old Felt to go long after it rubs the paper, as it always makes much more broken paper than meets the eye . . .

[1] This seems to allude to the method of finishing engine-sized paper which Dickinson patented in 1839. See p. 38.

'The packs can seldom be pressed too hard unless it is when a new Felt is put on, and then gentle pressure will do for 4 days or so. The packs should be lifted and put down plum and not drawn or pulled about, as that Rolls them . . .

'Dry Working. The paper should usually be hung 5 sheets thick and one spur a little over the other. The Lines should be kept tight and the Heat not too great *or too much Air in Summer*, particularly in fine Hot Weather. In fact to wet and sweep the Loft and keep the shutters shut, is frequently requisite in very hot weather . . .

'Tubsized paper should be hung only when cold and kept free from Sun and Air for 3 Days otherwise it will either take the size out or stain . . .

'*Produce of Machines.*

'A days work (12 Hours) of Demy at Great machine,[1] with the motion known by name *Demy*—28 Reams.
A day's work of double Foolscap 20 Reams . . .

'Day's work of Fine thick paper to be counted out in the wet state—say one Reel, and then reckon up from that.

'A day's work at Apsley Mills small machine, of 20 lbs. or thereabouts, is exactly for 12 hours work, 20 Reams each; a day's work of Royal of any common substance from 17 lbs. to 24 lbs. exactly, 15 Reams . . .

'Have an Eye to the packs. When 8 or 10 to press, keep Andrews and Rose at Work for the Night. Desire Reading to look over some single sheets Great Machine paper to see whether picked in Holes.

'Take a sheet from promiscuous packs every day to try Weight.

'The Sheets from the fire should weigh nearly one pound in Ten lighter than finished paper—for instance $21\frac{1}{2}$ lbs. Demy, 19 lb. brought from the fire, which has been found amply sufficient. We usually allow for shrinkage Great Machine paper $\frac{3}{4}$ of an Inch, by one In. in length. In little Machine paper $\frac{3}{4}$ by $1\frac{3}{4}$ . . .

'*Various causes that make damaged paper*.

'In Engine sized Great Apsley Machine papers:

'Fine wet stuff spoils at the first wet press in 3 ways—

'1st. It unmakes the paper again

---

[1] Evidently at Nash Mills, old No. 1.

'2nd. It deposits many flakes against the wet Doctor[1] which continue falling on the paper.

'3d. It occasions long streaks called Water Marks.

'At the 2d. pressure it is liable to felt, rub and stick to the top Cylinder. Upstairs it will pick in Holes. In the Loft it will most likely Cockle.

'To prevent this Evil, keep the tackle in good order and the plate full high in the Engine and do not suffer too much strong stuff to be got off to a mixing, neither let the stuff run long in the Engine after it is beat . . .

'If the packs are not carefully handled much paper is easily damaged on the top and bottom . . . The Women are much given to pulling the heaps of paper about to find out which will open best, and will dirty much. The men will also set it down where it gets soiled and run against it . . . In the Salle the Women will sometimes tear the corners off in stripping, and pick holes carelessly and put rough looking sheets to broken which will press even and cut out quite good if laid properly when overlooked . . .'

It was inevitable that an able and active-minded man at the height of his powers, with as great a knowledge of paper-making as John Dickinson had acquired, should try to improve some of its processes. In May 1811[2] he registered some further improvements in his cylinder machine, including a device by which the 'back' or vessel containing the pulp for supplying the cylinder was partitioned vertically, so that into each partition there flowed, from a separate vat, pulp of the colour required, the resultant sheet or web being thus formed in stripes. Other partitions made a horizontal striping of the paper possible. On 24 August 1814 he registered (with George Dickinson) apparatus for 'picking' or removing knots or lumps from paper or hard stuff.[3] The paper is led first over a small felt-covered wheel having a fast motion in the same direction as the paper;

[1] A Doctor is a device for cleaning cylinders as they revolve, with a blade fitted closely across the face of the press roll to remove any pieces of pulp that have adhered to the roll.
[2] Patent No. 3452.   [3] Patent No. 3839.

next over a straight edge; and then over felt-covered wooden cushions. Two rollers having iron bars brush the paper from above. The final reel is preferred of octagonal shape, the obtuse angles assisting in drawing the paper in a uniform direction. On 5 February 1821 Ann Dickinson tells us that George Dickinson 'was down here all the morning putting up Picking Machine to Mr. D's Great Machine, but it did not go well all day . . .' It was, indeed, never among the most successful of Dickinson's inventions, though a version of it, which caused wood, cork and other floating fragments to rise, and sand, grit and other heavy substances to sink in the vat, while the pulp was passed on free of both, was in use for a long time; its principle is incorporated in modern machines.

John Dickinson was fascinated by the qualities of the great webs of paper that came rolling off his machines and saw possibilities in them that had not yet been exploited. On 5 August 1817 he patented[1] a process for making paper for copperplate and letterpress printing, writing and drawing, and by using thicker materials, for boards like cardboard or pasteboard, by 'a process similar to veneering in cabinet-maker's work'. A reel full of moist paper is suspended over a machine making thicker paper; the end of the thin paper is laid upon the thick paper from the machine, and goes with it to the press rolls which unite them.[2] The process was so successful that the importation of French plate paper for copperplate prints came to an end.

Under the same patent he recorded his invention of machine sizing, by sizing paper in a roll by passing it through two size rollers. Previously, he states, 'the paper had been cut into

---

[1] Patent No. 4152. It also included modifications to his patent machinery for cutting paper—by cutting paper with a circular knife, and by cutting thicker paper and boards by circular knives on spindles, whose edges pass each other scissors fashion.

[2] The principle is the same as that of the modern machines at Croxley Mills which unite two webs of simultaneously made paper to form 'Evensyde' paper.

sheets; pressed in screw presses; hung upon lines to dry; sized by immersion in hot liquid size; the superfluous size pressed out by screw presses; and the sheets, after being separated and laid afresh, dried by hanging on the lines a second time'. His method, a modified version of which is still in use, was to pass the paper from the press rolls between sizing rollers rotating in a vessel containing the size and then to pass the paper to a cylinder heated by steam and to conduct it between a third pair of press rolls. A third clause in the patent covered the making of a thicker paper by drawing off two or more reels or lengths of paper together, drying, sizing strongly, and pressing.[1]

This patent of 1817, besides the veneered paper, contained the germs of two important inventions. The first of these was that of manufacturing cardboard from cylinder machines. The idea had been duly patented, but it was some time before the details were worked out. On 16 April 1821 Ann Dickinson records that 'they began making the paste for the experiment of Cardboards', on her kitchen stove; 'we had our dinner baked in consequence'. The next day she writes: 'They burnt the paste in Dairy Copper and were obliged to begin it again in kitchen and are making a terrible mess . . . They finished making 4 tubs of Paste having been all day at it . . .' On the 19th 'Mr. D. made a satisfactory experiment with the card machine'; and a week later, 'the Paste was boil'd by Steam beautifully'. Card-making began on 26 April, and experiments in its improvement continued through October and November.[2] On 4 November Ann tells us: 'Mr. D. up very late and finished a drawing for Card Machine.'

On 20 May 1824 Dickinson patented[3] a process for applying

---

[1] It is perhaps a machine of this kind that is alluded to in Ann Dickinson's diary for 30 November 1818: 'Mr. D. got his new double machine to work,' but the allusion may be to duplex paper. (See p. 38.)

[2] Diary, 28 October 1822.

[3] Patent No. 4959. It also included improvements to the circular cutters.

paste or other adhesive. Two lengths of paper, automatically unwound from near-by reels, pass up together and in contact between two press rollers, and just before their inner surfaces come together they receive a coating of paste from revolving brushes placed underneath, that receive their supply of paste from rollers capable of moving endwise while half-immersed in a trough of paste. Then, as the paper continues to pass up between the rollers, the pasted sides are pressed together. On 8 November 1824 Ann tells us: 'Dearest . . . wrote part of the Specifications for Card Machine', and soon afterwards its manufacture began at Apsley in a small building behind the office at the bottom of the yard, built out on wood piles over the sluice from the mill-head. On 4 January 1824 Ann Dickinson records a visit from Mr. Nash[1] to 'put dearest in the way to dye the papers'. By 1831 some eight or nine tons of boards were being produced at Apsley.

The making of this duplex paper was a closely guarded secret. Another paper-maker named Hall managed to get a fair idea of how it was done, and made a passable imitation. Some details, however, escaped him. He wrote to Dickinson for information, which was not supplied. A few days later an evangelist in a broad-brimmed hat turned up at the Mill and preached to the work-people as they came out. He expressed horror at finding they worked on Sundays, and when the day came round talked to the men on the sin of Sabbath-breaking, finally expressing a wish to go with them to see what the 'wicked work' was that they were doing. One foolish fellow took him in, and showed him. The next day the evangelist departed, his work done; and in the course of a few days Hall had perfected his process on the exact lines of Dickinson's. Dickinson heard the story of the

[1] Almost certainly William Nash, 1765–1824, who set up his Mill at Frogmore in 1817. His widow's will, dated 1831, is signed by John Dickinson as witness. See W. S. Shears, *William Nash of St. Paul's Cray*, 1950, pp. 2 and 9.

preacher, and had news of Hall's success. His language is said to have been fit to burn down the Mill. His conclusion was: 'This all comes of going to church.'

The second invention of which the germ was in the patent of 1817 was that of drying paper by steam heat. Meadows Taylor's account shows how empiric a process 'dry-work' was by the old methods. Nothing was more apt to hang up the deliveries of orders, for the machines often outran the dry-workers.[1] They were among the more irreplaceable men in the Mills. On 18 February 1821 Ann Dickinson writes: 'After breakfast Marshall came to tell Mr. D. that one of the dry workers had taken himself off after having just learnt the business, and that they had been so idle this week there was a great deal of Paper to hang. This was a source of great uneasiness to my dear Husband, and he went to work in the lofts himself till 2 o'c. . . .' Even Ann was inclined to look at the weather in terms of the drying shed. On 25 November 1823, for instance, she enters in her diary: 'It was as mild as a Summer Morning. Badly off for drying weather. Above 60 Packs at this Mill standing by. Mr. D. trying to dry by Steam.'

The production of paper on reels was to some extent rendered nugatory by the necessity of cutting it into sheets before it could be dried in the sheds. John Dickinson's 1817 patent had included the drying of his machine-sized paper round a cylinder heated by steam revolving in the same direction as the paper. The patent declares that it is 'for evaporating the water left in the paper after the pressure of the second pair of press rolls, and at the same time of its arrival at the third pair of press rolls the paper ought to be nearly dry, so dry that no humidity is perceptible to the touch'. The rate of travel of the paper, even when very thin, should not exceed 15 ft. a minute; more than one

---

[1] See letter of 16 September 1818 from John Dickinson to Joseph Applegath, of Messrs Lepard and Smith, explaining that drying difficulties have held up delivery of a large order.

steam cylinder could be used in series; their mechanism is exactly described.

On 1 November 1820 Thomas Bonsor Crompton was given a patent for drying-cylinders to be added to paper-machines, that seems remarkably close to the existing patent of John Dickinson. Dickinson took no action, but continued his own experiments. On 13 December 1823 Ann writes: 'Mr. D. wrote in Library. I assisted him in copying Patent for Steam rolls.' A week later she records: 'Dearest very busy trying to make steam rolls dry entirely', and two days later 'Dearest finds he shall succeed with the Steam rolls.'

Evidently there was some difficulty with Crompton's patent, for on 25 January 1824 she writes: 'Mr. Alderson a Counsel ... went to see our Steam rolls to compare with the Patent preparatory to giving his opinion as to the validity of it. He is a clever man but not very pleasant.' In the end Dickinson used his own process without patenting it: a plan that made him rather touchy about possible leakages of information. On 22 March 1824 Ann writes: 'Mr. Taylor told Mr. D. that Elliott had brot. a Tramping Paper Maker all over the Mills, which so enraged Mr. D. that he gave Elliott notice to keep off his Premises, and order'd poor Francis the Machine Man and Gates the Steam Roll man to be dismiss'd, a very proper example in my opinion.' Five days later, however, he forgave them.[1]

Many were at work to make the products of the paper-machine more closely resemble those of the hand-mould. John Dickinson and his brother were rivals in trying to make laid paper by machine. On 10 December 1823 Ann writes: 'Heard from dearest. G[eorge] D[ickinson] at some of his dirty tricks again trying to get rich to make him a laid roll and in consequence dearest tormented by his Mother.' On 5 March 1824 she wrote: 'Had long letter from dearest giving an acct. of the

[1] In 1822, Dickinson had been angry with a man who took Bryan Donkin, the engineer, over the Mills without leave. Diary, 15 October.

wretched paper G. has sent up for laid paper in imitation of his.'[1] In 1825 John and Christopher Phipps patented the dandy roll, that provided machine-made paper with a watermark, and Dickinson, together with all the other paper-makers, was thankful to use their invention. In 1829[2] Dickinson patented his own method of making laid paper, by improvements to his paper-machine, including a method of pressing out the water in the course of manufacture, by conducting the web by an endless felt between press rolls, where it received one or more pressures, one being given with the paper reversed, so that both sides should be glazed alike. This initiated the whole process of calendering.

At the same time he registered a method, stated to have been 'invented some years ago', for introducing threads of cotton, linen, or silk, web, lace or other material into the fabric of paper. The threads, wound on bobbins turned by hand, were drawn over grooves in the periphery of a roller running parallel to the paper-making cylinder. Once the thread-carrying paper had reached the endless felt that carried it off from the cylinder, the pull of the threads in the paper sufficed to turn the bobbins.

A third item in the same patent recorded an improvement in his paper-cutting machine by the use of a swinging frame with circular cutters acting against fixed straight cutters, by which several sheets could be cut at once from a single reel.

In the following year[3] he elaborated his patent for veneered paper to cover a duplex paper formed from two cylinders, each making paper webs, which are carried on together to press rolls to establish the adhesion between them. A machine of this kind

[1] On 28 December 1833, Patent No. 6535, George Dickinson patented a way of making laid paper by using threads or yarns on the endless web instead of wires. He had already, on 21 February 1828, patented (No. 5617) an improvement to the machine by giving a vertical motion to the endless web where it first received the pulp.

[2] Patent No. 5754, January 1829.

[3] 6 October 1830; Patent No. 6006.

was set up at Nash Mills before the end of the year. Two years later[1] he patented a machine for purifying pulp from knots, grit and other impurities by passing it in a dilute fluid state between longitudinal apertures, about $\frac{1}{115}$ of an inch wide, on the surface of a revolving cylinder that was in fact made 'like a squirrel cage' of circular hoops of endless spiral wire. A hollow copper float within the cylinder is given a rapid and constant up-and-down motion, but does not touch the wall of the cylinder. The method was revolutionary, but has only been exploited in recent times.

By this time John Dickinson was recognized in scientific circles, outside the little world of paper-making, as a man of notable inventive ability. As early as 1818 Sir Humphry Davy and Dr. Wollaston offered to propose him for election to the Royal Society, but he modestly refused. On 10 December 1824 Ann tells us: 'Dearest . . . went to the Royal Society with Mr. Solly[2] and was introduced to the President, was very civilly recd. and kindly treated by Dr. Wollaston, met many people he knew and liked it very much.' He did not stand, however, until 1845, when he was elected to the first scientific Society in the Kingdom. In 1833 he was elected to the Geological Society and the Beefsteak Club; and in 1852 to the Athenæum.

---

[1] 10 January 1832; Patent No. 6209. It also included further improvements to the cutting-machine.

[2] The Sollys of Serge Hill were Grover connexions.

IV

HOME PARK AND CROXLEY MILLS
1824–1836

IN 1824 John Dickinson completed his plans for reorganizing Nash Mills by the installation of a steam-engine. On 10 March Ann tells us: 'Dearest . . . was in Gt. Mill till past one, to start the new Mill on the water, it goes off remarkably well.' Two days later: 'Dearest . . . was in the Mill some hours starting new [beating] Engine which is the last and makes the Mill now quite complete.' On 18 March: 'Dearest . . . wrote to Marshall [the Nash Mills Manager] about raising his salary in the event of his turning out 800 Rms. per week from the Mill.' Fortunately an order from the Bible Society for 700 reams came in the day the engine was started.

At Apsley, meanwhile, the forwarding by the canal was improved; on the last day of 1824 Ann wrote: 'Went to wharf on business at Apsley; find it go very well and like the whole set out very much.'

John Dickinson now had Apsley and Nash Mills at work under steam-power at the manufacture of paper, and Batchworth at the preparation of half-stuff. They did not satisfy his ambition, and he planned the erection of a third mill, about a mile below Nash, where there was water-power available. On 11 October 1824 he consulted Thomas Longman, as his former partner's executor, and received his consent; on the 26th he had a satisfactory interview on the subject with old Andrew Strahan. On the 30th Ann tells us: 'Dearest went to call on Ld. Essex about this Mill and was very kindly and graciously recd. and promis'd to give his assistance as far as it was wanted. A cold windy day, but dearest is in gt. spirits at the result of his interview.' The next day '. . . He walk'd down to the spot he has fix'd on for his Mill and drew a new plan of it'. By the middle of November he had 'smooth'd the way for his Mill site with the neighbourhood, and in some degree with the Tenants'.

Building proceeded, and on 19 June 1825 Ann wrote: 'Saw Durrant [the foreman of the building] about the children's laying the first brick of the new Mill.' The next day Samuel, aged five, laid the first brick, and William, aged four, the second. The land had been bought from Lord Essex, and on 14 August he wrote, in answer to an inquiry from Dickinson, to suggest that the new factory should be called 'Home Park Mills', to perpetuate the name borne by the land when it had been granted by Edward IV to his ancestors, it having originally formed part of the park of the royal palace built by Henry III at King's Langley. A public footpath led through the Mill land and helped to establish a less austere tradition for Home Park than that prevalent at Apsley and Nash, both more directly under Dickinson's eye. Legend says that the Mill was once hurriedly closed to let the workers follow the Hertfordshire Hunt, which had found near by. The land round it was still agricultural. Four pairs of cottages were built close at hand for the work-people and let at half a crown a week. Six more were built in the village street to the east of Nash Mills; and a set of fifteen round a little square at Doolittle, on the main road between the Red Lion and Apsley.[1]

On 23 January 1826 Dickinson was able to open the communication between the Canal and the new mill-tail at Home Park. On 7 May he came to London 'very uneasy at leaving the new Mills as he is putting in the Cut-out to his Machine Wheel'. On 28 July the new mill was started. On 3 August Ann writes: 'Had a kind letter from dearest . . . The E[ast] I[ndia] Company are

[1] These have since been demolished and the site is now a car-park for the Mills.

about giving him another large order of 10,000 Rms. which is an unlook'd for piece of good fortune just as his new Mill is starting.' A week later she records: 'Dearest up at 3 and at New Mill and set the people to work and came back and laid down for an hour . . . He set off for London in gig at 9, calling at Mill on his way. Has started both machines well.' In the beginning Home Park chiefly produced the special cards required for Jacquard weaving, for which there was a considerable demand in the North, and wrapping paper for textiles.

The year 1826 was a time of great anxiety for Dickinson as for all men of business. The country banks, of which Grover's was one,[1] were hit first. On 13 December 1825 Ann was writing in her diary: 'This is the most awful period in the commercial world that ever was known. The oldest and best establish'd houses are falling one after another and great fears are entertain'd for every Country bank in the country. My dear Father will I fear be run upon. Williams of More Park has stopp'd, and Whittaker the bookseller to-day. My dear has a large sum lock'd up there tho' he will not ultimately lose it.' The next day she continues . . . 'The accts. from the City getting more gloomy, and Dearest entertains great alarm for my Fa's Bank. A meeting of the Merchants and Traders took place at the Mansion House, at which resolutions were pass'd to support the public credit and Bankers as far as possible. Dearest wrote these to my Fa. by post recommending him to endeavour to have the same sort of thing set on foot on his behalf.'

This news, and money that Dickinson sent from London, kept the Bank going through an anxious week. Dorrien's sent down £4,000 in a post-chaise on the 15th, and advanced £10,000 more; and the gentry and tradesmen of Hempstead met that day at the Town Hall and passed resolutions promising their support to Grover's Bank. His daughter recorded the

[1] Harry Grover's partner was by this time his son-in-law William Smith, Pollard having retired.

meeting in her diary that night. 'Mr. Collett offer'd to sell stock to the amount of £10,000 if my Fa. should want and many similar kind offers were made him and everything was done which a kind and sympathizing set of neighbours cd. do, and may God reward them!'

Four days later she wrote from the Grover house in London. 'Mr. D. came up very unexpectedly by 1 o'clock, being so uneasy at the state of things he could not stay down there . . . He is in a very anxious state about some of the booksellers. God protect him from these disasters! . . . Dearest's anxiety seems to increase. God preserve us! for we are in great jeopardy, and very likely to fall victims to the speculations of these rogues of Booksellers who have been gambling in speculations out of their trade.' Hurst and Robinson, indeed, who started the débâcle, had been speculating in hops; Constable and Hurst and Robinson had backed each other's bills; and Ballantynes, who were Constable's printers, had raised money on Constable's credits.[1] Those three firms were so involved that if one fell, all did; and beyond them stretched the ramifications of their creditors and discounters and suppliers. On 21 December Ann Dickinson writes: 'Dearest still in great anxiety about H. & R. the Bkrs. too refuse his disc[oun]t business. May God preserve and console him!' Two days later: 'Dearest . . . never came to dinner and at past 7 he came in very much fatigued and harass'd. Those Paternoster Booksellers have caused him gt. embarrassment by refusing to allow him to open his acct. at Smith Payne and Smiths as he had arranged and he has been obliged in consequence to apply to Mr. S[trahan] for supplies till he can look round again . . . He is made quite ill by these vexations.'

On 13 January 1826 she wrote: 'This is an eventful day for my dearest. Pray Heaven to protect and bring him out of his difficulties! . . . My dear Husband came home very late to dinner and in a state of the greatest alarm, the house of Hurst

[1] See S. Gwynn, *Life of Sir Walter Scott*, 1930, p. 316.

and Robinson having stopp'd payment and he having an immense sum in Bills on it, also for the consequences that must follow to others which will involve him in fresh difficulties. He set off for Highgate to see Hurst about it at 9 o'clock at night, and when he return'd he had not done any good, in fact he has received and drawn him in to a most dreadful scrape, and without the assistance of very powerful friends he must stop.'

The next day she continues: 'My dearest went this morng. to my Father and he wrote off to my Uncle Ralph Day to ask his assistance which I trust in God will be accorded. Mr. S[trahan] is very violent but I still hope he will do all that is necessary. My dear is harrass'd almost to death . . . My dearest was at the Warehouse till near 12 tonight and came home unhappy and uneasy.' Two days later she writes: 'Uncle Ralph sends permission to my dear Fa. to use the money he had impower'd him to sell out for my drs. benefit.' The next day: 'My dr. Fa. is to meet Mr. Strahan and Longman on my dear's business. They have had a long conference in which Mr. S. has made out a list of grievances as long as my arm and succeeded to perfection with my Fa. in making himself out an Angel and my dearest a Demon—but God knows the truth and will one of these days make it appear.'

Andrew Strahan, indeed, was himself having an anxious time. Hurst and Robinson's failure involved Constable and Cadell, and Cadell had once been William Strahan's partner and was still the family's debtor. Their combined failure hit nearly everyone in the publishing trade, including Sir Walter Scott, who was a partner in Constable's and in their printers, Ballantynes, who also failed.

John Dickinson was a little more fortunate. On 19 January his wife thankfully records: '. . . Dearest seems better to-day owing to the Secy. to Bible Socy. telling him that he had sent an order to Cambridge for bibles on condition of their using his Machine paper. This is good news just now.'

On 2 February, 'Dearest attended a meeting of Whittaker's Creditors and it was then agreed to put his affairs in the hands of Trustees and not make him a Bankrupt. He seems altogether in better spirits about his own business.' On 7 February: 'Dearest . . . dined at the Mansion House where he was honor'd by having his health drunk for his eminence in his business and Science. His clothes came but just in time and I was very much flurried by his being so angry about them.'

A week later, however, things were 'more and more gloomy in the City'. On the 15th Ann records: 'Three more great Merchants gone to-day, of them Goldschmid for 2 millions of money.' On the 21st she writes: 'A great many more Houses in the City gone and Sr. John Perrins among the number. Mr. D. fearing this would cause a run on my Father's Bank sent G. off this afternoon with 1,000 sovereigns for him.'

Grover's Bank was saved, but the Dickinsons' troubles continued. Their son Samuel died in the summer, aged six. Soon afterwards, on 16 July, Ann wrote: 'A number of disasters have befallen the Mills lately and my dr. Husband seems worried on all sides . . . The Steam Engine boiler burst and that was laid still, then the N. Mill great water wheel shaft broke and that Mill is still. Also the Batchworth Water Wheel shaft broke down and that is still, besides many other vexations in his business.' A month later she writes: 'Dearest in great trouble about the New Mill as the Machine goes unequal. He kept us there till near 10 o'clock.'

Sir Walter Scott was left, as a man of honour, to work to pay the £40,000 of debts made by Constable and Cadell as well as himself. *Woodstock* was published by Longman's in the summer of 1826, and *Napoleon* in the late autumn. Sir William Forbes got him out of his immediate difficulties and by Christmas Constable had launched a scheme by which the copyrights were sold to the trustees of Scott's estate, by which his creditors were ultimately repaid in full.

Meanwhile Dickinson was doing what he could with Constable's affairs. On 5 September 1827 Scott mentions in his Journal: 'Mr. Dickinson, paper-maker, who has undertaken that the London creditors who hold Constable's bills will be satisfied with 10s. in the pound. This would be . . . to purpose, for 6s. 8d. is provided, and they can have no difficulty about 3s. 4d. These debts, for which I am legally responsible, though no party to their contraction, amount to £30,000 odd. Now if they can be cleared for £15,000 it is just so much gained. This would be a great step to freedom.'

In February 1830 Scott had a severe seizure, followed by months of illness. In June the threat of further illness caused him to resign his judicial post. Just at this time John Dickinson was again enabled to help the great man. Scott records in his Journal for June 3: 'I saw Mr. Dickinson on Tuesday, a right plain sensible man. He is so confident in my matters, that, being a large creditor himself, he offers to come down, with the support of all the London creditors, to carry through any measure that can be devised for my behoof. Mr. Cadell showed him that we are four years forward in matter prepared for the press.' Little more than two years later Scott was dead, worn out by his self-imposed labours on his creditors' behalf.[1]

Long before this John Dickinson was already embarking on further projects. As early as 14 December 1826 Ann records: 'Dearest . . . set off for [Cambridge] . . . to treat with Caius Coll. for some of their Land for a site for a new Mill, which he contemplates setting up with *God's blessing* below Cashio Bridge.' The site was at Croxley, to the south-west of the little market town of Watford, some five miles by canal from Home Park. A private Act of Parliament had to be obtained to permit the purchase,[2] but by the autumn of 1828 building had begun.

[1] On the friendly relations between Dickinson and the Cadells at this time see T. Besterman, *The Publishing Firm of Cadell and Davies*, 1793—1836, Oxford, 1938, p. xvii.

[2] Royal Assent given, 19 June 1828.

The site lies between the stream of the Gade and the canal. A mill-head was constructed, half a mile long, to Cassio Bridge, and a mill-tail cut across Common Moor to join the canal below the lock about a mile from the mills.

The foundations of the mill proved more difficult and expensive to construct than Dickinson (who as usual carried out the building himself) had anticipated. On 15 October Ann writes: 'Dearest . . . has been just 5 weeks about this work and of that only 9 days at the brickwork, so great a quantity of water hinder'd their work. The foundations are now thank God out of water and he may leave them to others.' Young Charles Longman was, in fact, sent to live near by to supervise the work. Lord Ebury, who lived at Moor Park, had a view of the Mill, and to meet his objections it was provided with 'an Egyptian Front', with two massive columns, and an entablature of painted stucco.[1]

Dickinson's troubles over Croxley were not over. On 5 December Ann writes: 'My dr. husband . . . is I regret to say plunged in more troubles by an injunction from the Ct. of Ch[ancer]y to restrain his works on the Moor and new Mill, which he is obliged to defend and get over!' Fortunately on 10 December the injunction was dissolved.

At last, on 10 August 1829, Dickinson was able to give a grand dinner to seventy-six of his friends and relations in the new Salle at Croxley. Grovers, Longmans, Spottiswoodes and all his chief customers were there, and room was even found for his poor clerical relations. By the next year the Mill was at work. Here, as at Home Park, Dickinson at once built two rows of four cottages to let to his work-people at his usual weekly rental of half a crown.

Croxley was hardly fully at work before all the Mills fell into jeopardy. On 29 November 1830 a gang of machine breakers,

[1] This has since been demolished, but may be seen in the photograph reproduced in plate 18.

men of the 'Swing Riots', marched upon the mills in the Gade Valley from Buckinghamshire. Dickinson hurriedly organized a defence force for each of his mills under the direction of General Beckwith, an old Peninsular officer, who happened to be staying with him; but happily the rioters, while still north of Apsley, saw the red coats of the Old Berkeley Hunt in the distance, took them for mounted soldiers sent to defend the mills, and turned back again.

Once more things settled down peaceably, and on 21 April 1834 Dickinson's elder daughter Fanny could record in her diary: 'Trades Union Meeting. All pass'd off quietly.'

In 1833 Dickinson turned his attention to remodelling the half-stuff Mill at Batchworth, with the aid of the architect William Tite.[1] Dickinson lived at the Mill for a time, with his only surviving son John—who had just left Eton—in the hope of interesting him in the processes of paper-making. Between 1835 and 1837 he built a second half-stuff mill at Manchester, to clean and use the waste from the local cotton-mills. Its personnel gave him and his partner a good deal of trouble. On 3 April 1838 Charles Longman wrote[2] to Dickinson: '... I fear they are a bad set at Manchester. I wish that we had entirely our own men. Our own men ought to have their cottages and be in every way as separate from the natives as possible. We shall have to send more down in August. I don't know if you have made arrangements about building for them ...'

In 1835 a new large paper-machine was substituted for the small one at Apsley, and in 1838 Croxley was enlarged to produce fourteen tons of paper a week.

The troubles over water supply continued. On the first day of 1834 Fanny Dickinson wrote in her diary: 'The New Year opens unpromisingly—this short water and poor Papa's long face are terrible. God bless us all and have mercy upon us!' In

[1] In the same year a new wharf was made at Nash Mills.
[2] J.D.E.

that year, too, Thomas Telford, the engineer, reporting to the House of Commons on the Metropolitan water supply, said that the Gade at Hunton Bridge was already 'infected by the deleterious substances used for paper mills, and could not be used'.

The year 1833 saw a great upward swing in the firm's fortunes. The balance sheet on 30 June was as follows:

	£	s.	d.		£	s.	d.
Stock of paper in London	10,907	19	5	Bills accepted	17,844	6	5
Debts owing to J.D.& Co.	74,154	0	0	Debts owing by J. D. & Co.	6,987	9	2
Bills and cash belonging				Debts in Mill accounts	23,102	14	9
to the firm	25,172	14	7	Balance in favour	96,708	17	1
Stock of Rags	34,408	13	5				
	144,643	7	5		144,643	7	5

The same level was maintained for at least three years. There were changes, too, in Dickinson's own circumstances. His father died in May 1828, but left all his money to his widow. She handed over to him his father's escritoire to stand in his room at the Old Bailey; it is still in use in the Director's offices at Apsley. In 1831 Andrew Strahan died, leaving an enormous fortune. He remembered all the Dickinsons in his will, leaving £5,000 to old Mrs. Dickinson, £4,000 to John, £2,000 to each of his married sisters, and £1,500 each to his unmarried brother and sister. In 1835 his residuary legatees[1] assented to John Dickinson's proposal to pay off his debt to the Strahan estate.

Ann Dickinson had inherited a little money from her uncle, Ralph Day, invested in the 3 per cents. Dickinson reinvested it in his own business, promising to pay cumulative interest on it at 5 per cent for his son William. After the child died, she heard no more of it, and indeed it was legally her husband's.

[1] Letter from John Spottiswoode, June 1835. J.D.E. In July 1837 Dickinson paid off £6,500 to the executor for the mortgage and interest on Batchworth, and £375 for a half-year's interest on the mortgage on Croxley. The Batchworth mortgage was renewed to other clients of his lawyers.

His many activities were made a little easier for Dickinson, now in his fifties, by the possession of a London house. It had been all very well to ride up to London for the day as a young man, or to travel there in his gig in his thirties and in his carriage in his forties, but now he found it too tiring to shuttle constantly between the Mills and the Old Bailey, and preferred to spend a night, or sometimes a few weeks, in town. The Grovers had long had a convenient if unfashionable town house in Bedford Row, and in 1825 he took No. 22 in the same street: an old and rather dilapidated house, to whose architectural beauties Ann proved blind. Then, on 7 November 1834, the Dickinsons left Nash House; and in the following spring Charles Longman brought his bride to it. For a time Dickinson made London his home; when he needed to spend more than a day at the Mills he slept in a room he kept at Nash Mills Farm.

Even from London travel was not yet easy. He was still in constant touch with his Edinburgh customers, yet the journey to see them was long and even sometimes dangerous. On 23 October 1826 Ann wrote: 'My dear husband started for Edinb^h. in the Steam Packet, which served him exactly as he was before in the former trip—viz. he was beaten about 66 hours and then put into Bridlington and obliged to find his way to York and from thence to Edin^h. after suffering immensely from fatigue and worry and sickness.'

A letter[1] from John Dickinson in London to Charles Longman at Nash Mills, written on 27 May 1833 after a visit to Scotland, shows how important these journeys were to the prosperity and progress of the business.

'Dear Sir,
'I arrived here this evening and left all friends in the North favorably dispos'd, but the makers there are really turning out capital paper, better than ever I saw before. Oliver and Boyd order'd 200 Rms of their Dble flat, and want it immediately—

[1] J.D.E.

their last lot but one was fluey and very inadequately sized—the last lot was better but some of that unequally sized. It is very important to attend to all these particulars now, for the paper undergoes a strict ordeal and comparison there. This is exceedingly wanted, and I don't know whether they have any in the Old Bailey. Pray get it in hand immed[y]. and have wrappers filed for their Presses will be at a stand.

'I was so exceedingly taken up with business and Mr. W. at Edin. that I could not possibly write from there. I miss'd some of the people, but recd. £5515 independent of Mr. W. and Cadell . . . I think the cards will do well in Scotland, but it is extraordinary what a quantity of the enamell'd cards they use there. I think I must find out how they are done, and perhaps we could add it without much difficulty. We could command Dble. price for them.

'As for the bleaching I am more puzzled than ever. Both the Scotch bleachers condemn the puffers and steam Boiling altogether. I consum'd a day nearly in getting to each of them, and was well receiv'd tho' rather shy at first. They were 40 miles nearly apart, and did not work for the same market. They united in a horror of Lime, and they agree in the importance of the alkaline processes, but they do not care about making it quite caustic. They wash well between each process, but they both agree in the necessity of exposure to day light, which the goods require twice in the process. They are first spread on the grass, then hung up out of doors till nearly dry.'[1]

Dickinson's interest in technical processes was lively as ever, but his own inventions were fewer. In 1835 he and his millwright, William Long Tyers, took out a patent[2] covering two devices. The first was the use of magnets for extracting particles of iron and steel from pulp, as it flowed slowly in a dilute state in a stream less than two inches deep along a trough of thin copper some six or eight feet long, with fixed rows of horse-shoe magnets beneath. The second was an improvement to Dickinson's cylinder paper-making machine by which fibres were

[1] A long account of the process follows.
[2] No. 6866, 24 July 1835.

deposited transverse and not parallel to the movement of the cylinder, 'by partitioning off the vat of pulp into scallops and so feeding it that there is a current along each scallop at right angles, or nearly so, with the cylinder'.

A great change was coming to England: a change that was to confirm the wisdom of Dickinson's choice of site for his Mills and to assure their future. In 1825 George Stephenson's engine first drew a train—and it weighed ninety-two tons and included thirty-four wagons—at ten miles an hour along the Stockton and Darlington Railroad, with a signalman on horseback riding in front. In 1830 the Manchester and Liverpool Railway was opened by the first modern locomotive, the Rocket. Then the London and Birmingham Railway was planned to follow the Grand Junction Canal up the valley of the Gade. Fanny Dickinson's diary records that in August 1833 they drove out several times 'to see the railroad'. On 13 July 1836 it was opened as far as Boxmoor: four days later the Dickinsons travelled to London by it. A year later John's younger daughter, Harriet, returned from school by train, travelling in an open first-class coach in seventy-five minutes from Euston to Boxmoor. The next year the line reached Birmingham and trains sped over it at twenty miles an hour. A new and swifter means of transit for his raw materials and his finished products was assured to Dickinson's Mills, both North and South.

In 1838 John Dickinson could state:[1] 'The practice in our trade is to deliver our paper at all considerable places to which there is an easy access by canal or other water carriage, or by railway carriage. I do a good deal of business in Scotland, and I deliver paper at Edinburgh, Glasgow, Dundee and Aberdeen . . . We do not undertake to send anything by waggons, or the ordinary land conveyance.'

[1] Commission on the Post Office, 2 March 1838, answer No. 2438.

V

ABBOT'S HILL
1836–1840

JOHN DICKINSON's home life at this time was no longer happy. His wife had lost beloved children in 1811, 1813, 1826 and 1832; she had become something of a nervous invalid, deeply interested in her own health, and combining her innate quick temper with a new querulousness. She had always been a pious woman and now her religion tended to become both sentimental and superstitious; on most Sundays she used to decide that she felt too ill to go to church, then spend the morning in wondering if God would forgive her. John Dickinson, though no churchman, had for his mother's sake a general tolerance of religion, but he had no patience with religiosity or hypochondria. Ann's case was not helped by her knowledge of this; and she came to accept the fact that John loved his children more than herself.

In 1836 Dickinson began to build himself a fine new house, which he called Abbot's Hill, on the eminence that rose to the east of Nash Mills, where he had bought some 125 acres. He was, as usual, his own architect; he employed for his building the dark grey stone setts that had originally been used for a part of the London and Birmingham Railway, and had later been replaced by sleepers. John Dickinson had a theory that no house should have more than one door to the outside world. He followed it, not unreasonably, in his workmen's cottages, and remained faithful to it in his own great house, which, so long as he was alive, had only one remarkably impressive oaken outside door.

Ann Dickinson wrote that 'the odious house' was built against her declared wishes. On 16 July 1837 she records: 'There is a great deal of company of one sort or other, and that makes servants necessary, and clothing of all sorts, and we are to keep up a certain appearance and enter into Society, but he does not expect to pay for it, and how we are to manage in this great house I dread to think.' They moved into Abbot's Hill in October 1837. On 12 July she wrote: 'It is, as I always expected it would be—every thing is half finish'd and left for me to make out with as I may—and I am to make preparations for large parties with worse than no conveniences for every thing is a hindrance and out of order . . . There is no water in the cistern that supplies the boiler . . . and the supply [of water] is insufficient for the Stable and kitchen. The rooms will not be ready for the company. I have a new cook . . . and Mr. D. [is] sulky because I apply to him to repair his own works . . . I am surrounded by new servants and have to teach them everything . . .'

Dickinson, as his mother's son and a man of business, believed in hospitality; Ann dreaded it. A constant refrain in her diary is: 'Quiet day, thank God!' None the less the new house saw a great deal of entertaining, especially at week-ends—Murrays, Lockharts, Longmans and all the rest of the London printing and publishing set, as well as any number of relations.[1]

John Dickinson had no sympathy with housekeeping difficulties, but exercised an absolute dictatorship in hospitality as in all else. He was apt to be precipitate in his planning; in 1840 Ann and he had a great quarrel, which nearly ended in separation, all over half a buck sent by the Evanses from Bosworth, that arrived after the parties he had arranged for its consumption had taken place.

[1] The technical acquaintances usually came only for the day. For instance, on 20 June 1840, Fanny records: 'By the 12 o'c. train came down some Snobs to see the Mills—viz. Mr. and Mrs. Holtzapfell, Cowper (the engin^r) and a nephew of his.'

He was too set on his own opinions to court popularity in Hertfordshire. On 22 October 1841 his wife wrote in her diary: 'Was restless in Night thinking of Position Mr. D. has placed himself by his foolish standing out about the Corn Laws, not meaning to forsake his party and yet leaving them when most wanted, and not forwarding his own cause nor influencing others —but in short giving himself up to be cut out of the circle of country Gentlemen, and allowing his position in Society to be taken by Longman . . . It is bad for his family, and he will never regain what he has lost. I don't like to dwell on it, and never felt any of his oddities more annoying.'

Gradually, however, John Dickinson came to be accepted in Hertfordshire society in his own right and not merely as a Grover relation. Although no churchman he did his duty in subscribing towards the building of a church at Leverstock Green; in 1847 he built a little school in Nash Mills village at his own expense. He gave the land, just by King's Langley Railway Station, for the erection of the Booksellers' Provident Retreat. Its opening on 3 September 1845 may be said to mark his acceptance as a local landowner.

John and his wife shared many anxieties over their one surviving son. He grew up into a moody, difficult man, of a pretty wit and an irritable temper, who could work with no one, least of all his father.

In 1837 he began to work at the Old Bailey, but it was not a success. On 27 January 1838 Ann writes: 'I cannot disguise from myself that while we enjoy many blessings (many more than we deserve) yet they are sour'd by the uncertain situation of my poor son. God bless him, what is to become of him? . . . I try to hope the best . . . but still if he truly loved me would he not have endeavour'd to acquire some insight into his Father's business and concerns which wd. have enabled him to take some burden from his shoulders, and to stand at some future day in his shoes, for he knows my anxiety on that head—but he is listless and indifferent, stubborn and selfish—is fond of indulgence, but I fear would forget those who indulge, if need be.'

In 1839 young John had a breakdown in health, and went to recover and amuse himself at Bonn. In 1840 he returned, to set up his own bachelor establishment in London. In May 1841, having been ill 'in mind and body' he retired to Italy with the declared intention of living there. In June 1842 he wrote thence to offer to enter the business, saying that he had been dangerously ill but was now better. Two years later he was working at the Old Bailey and hating it. He stayed there until July 1845, when he threw it all up and went abroad again in search of health. He was in Paris through the Revolution of 1848, and sent home a series of able letters, which were printed in *The Times*, to describe his experiences and summarize his opinions. Harriet Dickinson was greatly interested and wrote to her cousin Sebastian in India:[1] 'How happily has England been preserved in the midst of these surrounding troubles! . . . Not that her state is altogether prosperous and secure. Wherever you look evils exist within her, threatening future consequences terrible to contemplate. Every year seems to accumulate luxury on the one hand and distress and misery on the other. Who can wonder if even a false hope of bettering their condition should tempt the famishing multitude from their duty?

'On the whole we do not have to witness much distress about here. Papa's Mills give employment to so many, and the people in this village[2] having both better and more regular pay than the agricultural labourers, get many little comforts about them and are not reduced to starvation at the first disaster. You see books on their tables and muslin blinds in their windows, very often, and altogether a degree of civilization about the place which it is very comforting to witness. I should be miserable if the wealth that built this house had been made by "grinding the faces of the poor". As it is we know the very prosperity of this

[1] J.D.E.   [2] Nash Mills.

part of the country is bound up in the prosperity of our Mills.'

John Dickinson had clearly no cause to nourish great hopes for the commercial future of his son. His two daughters, however, were handsome and intelligent and gave him just cause for pride. The elder, Frances Elizabeth, always called Fanny, was a gay pretty creature, with a great taste in dress, an excellent dancer, and a moderate musician with a small repertoire—Weber's *Invitation to the Waltz* for dinner-parties and a little Haydn for Sunday evenings. She was genuinely fond of John Dickinson— 'my dear gov'ner'—and was probably his favourite child. Grandmama Dickinson tried to marry her to various smart young officers in the Rifles, stationed at Woolwich, and her father more shrewdly destined her for one of the young Murrays or Blackwoods whom he assiduously invited to Abbot's Hill. She had many proposals but refused them all. There was, however, a Captain Barlow whom Fanny used to meet at her grandmother's, who had a nephew, Frederick Pratt Barlow, who was a London solicitor and Secretary to the Blackwall Railway. On 1 September 1840 her cousin Anne Evans wrote to Mary Phelps in Madeira[1] to report their engagement as 'the latest family news—so I will tell you all about the gentleman who has been so *unusually* fortunate. He is of highly respectable connexions (I don't mean aristocratic), his father is a Magistrate and greatly respected, living at Kensington, and the family is—we hear from the Dickinsons—a most agreeable and delightful one. They live, Fanny tells me, in very comfortable style, without being fine. And now for the young gentleman, which is of far more consequence. He is a good specimen, I think, of his family and appeared, from the little I saw of him, sensible and aimiable. He is very young, tho' the eldest son—younger even I hear than Fanny—...He is a lawyer (*not* a barrister).' Fred Pratt Barlow practised in Doctors' Commons, and in November 1840 entered

[1] The letter has kindly been lent me by my cousin Miss Josephine Phelps.

into partnership with a man named Justin. His father was a wealthy wine merchant and a Director of the Great Western Railway, living at 24 Kensington Square.[1] They married in 1840, and settled in comfort and style in a brand new house at 17 Rutland Gate. Once his daughter was married John Dickinson gave up the house in Bedford Row and took chambers for a *pied-à-terre* for himself when business kept him in London.

By 1840 the family had come to realize that young John would never make a career in the business. His aunt, Anne Evans, had four sons to place in the world, and knew that her schoolmaster husband had shot his bolt in educating them well at his own school. On 28 January 1840 she wrote to her brother to broach the question of one of them entering the service of John Dickinson & Co. She had in mind her second son, godson and namesake of John Dickinson. All her sons had good academic brains, but John alone among them had the Brissac commonsense and capacity for hard work. He longed for Oxford and the Bar; but because of his qualities was condemned to renounce them, for his uncle accepted the proposal. John Evans entered the accounts office at Nash Mills on 1 May 1840 under Mr. Tyers. He started work every morning at seven, breakfasted at eight, dined between twelve and one, and got back to his lodgings in Mr. Tyers's house some time between six and ten. By the spring of 1845 he was earning a fixed salary of £200 a year and had a little house of his own in the village, No. 1 Nash Mills.

John Evans's scholarly and unpractical father was not happy in the choice of his son's career. There was a profound antipathy between him and his brother-in-law, based on the sense that they valued different things. Old Evans wrote in his commonplace book[2] at this time: 'The Manufacturers, masters and men,

---

[1] He died in 1855; his other son continued the business.
[2] In the writer's possession.

the worshippers and the victims of Mammon, are and will be the curse of this country. The former, little or half-educated, knowing as much of the nature and value of our institutions as they do of the "Institute of Timour", not only "hasting to be rich", but breathless and almost sleepless in the pursuit, fall into a snare, indeed, the snare of godless and heartless indifference to everything but money. The latter grinding in helpless bondage, and making their children pass through the fire, with their minds dark to blackness, and for the most part unconscious that they have *souls*, look neither to moral duty, nor future responsibility, but would gladly to-morrow break down the barriers of civilization and humanity, to revenge themselves on a social state, which keeps them "in misery and iron", and scramble in blood for the property of all those who may thrive by their ignorance and irreligion. There is a fearful remark of Sir W. Scott in his Journal:[1] "God's justice is requiting, and will yet further requite, those who have blown up this country into a state of insubstantial opulence, at the expense of the health and morals of the lower classes."'

Arthur Evans had lived through the years of the French Revolution, and saw industrial England in terms of aristocratic France. He did not realize that so long as masters worked as hard as men, and so long as the masters-to-be of the next generation worked with men at the same task, social change would be brought about by gradual and peaceful means. His son, working at his high desk in Nash Mills office, could have told him that a new kind of society was being brought into being, with its classes as interdependent as those of feudal England.

John Dickinson had already gained some experience of dealing with Government departments otherwise than as a supplier. In August 1831 he had presided over a meeting of manufacturers of paper and pasteboard in England and Wales, to send

[1] At the close of Lockhart's life of him, p. 392 [Lockhart's *Life of Scott* was published in 1838].

a memorial to the Government asking for a repeal of the Excise Duty on paper, 'in consequence of the unprecedented depression of their manufacture'. The paper duty,[1] which had first been imposed under Queen Anne, fell heavily on the maker. A contemporary account[2] shows how it was levied. 'Every maker is required by law to obtain from the Excise officer a label to be pasted upon each ream of paper, declaring the class of paper and weight of paper . . . and be liable to a penalty of £200 if he cannot account for every label delivered to him by the Excise.' He had to use a departure stamp containing the number of his Mill on the official register and the date when the paper was sent away from it; and to keep an elaborate daybook for the excisemen's inspection. The method, dating from the days of paper-making by hand in small mills, had become almost intolerable by 1835, when there were 82 machines in the United Kingdom annually producing 24,475 tons of machine-made paper, and 430 vats producing 11,215 tons of hand-made paper.[3] It had the further effect of preventing advances in the technique of printing. In 1835, for example, Rowland Hill patented[4] a rotary machine for printing on the long rolls of paper produced by machine, but his invention could not be exploited because the Government stamp was levied by the sheet.

The duty was in itself heavy enough: $3\frac{1}{2}$d. a lb. on all paper. It was counterpoised by an import duty of 3d. a lb. on brown paper made from old rope and cordage, and of 9d. a lb. on all other kinds of paper. In 1825, however, there had been a move to remove this protective duty. On 29 April Ann writes: 'Dearest off at 6 this morng. and rode to Town to attend an appointment with Mr. Huskisson about the paper Duties.' On the following

[1] For an account of it see C. D. Collet, *History of the Taxes on Knowledge*.

[2] Statement at the Official Inquiry, 1835, quoted Shears, p. 19.

[3] Dard Hunter, p. 526. By 1833 Bryan Donkin had made thirty-eight paper-machines, and by 1850, 191.

[4] Patent No. 6762, 12 August 1835. *Life of Rowland Hill*, I, p. 225.

day she continues, 'He has succeeded with Mr. Huskisson who has consented to continue the protecting duties on papers'.

The manufacturers were further hit by a duty of 5s. a ton on the import of rags 'fit only for making paper and paste-board'. This was the more severe since they could not meet their needs by English rags alone. An article of 1833[1] declares: 'The rags of our own country do not furnish a fifth part of what we consume in the manufacture of paper. France, Holland, and Belgium prohibit, under severe penalties, the exportation of rags, because they require them for their own long-established manufactories. Spain and Portugal also prohibit their exportation. Italy and Germany furnish the principal supplies of linen rags, both to Great Britain and the United States. They are exported from Bremen, Hamburgh, Rostock, Ancona, Leghorn, Messina, Palermo and Trieste. They arrive in our ports in closely packed bags, containing each about four hundredweight, which, according to the respective qualities of the rag, are marked SPFF, SPF, FF, FX and FB. There are many varieties of rag even in these divisions; and their qualities are pretty clear indications of the state of comfort and cleanliness in particular districts and countries. The linen rags of England are generally very clean, and require little washing and no bleaching, before they are ground into pulp; the Sicilian rags, on the contrary, are originally so dirty, that they are washed in lime before they are fit for the foreign market. The greater portion of the rags from the North of Europe are so dark in their colour and so coarse in their texture, that it is difficult to imagine how they could have formed part of any inner garments; while those, on the other hand, which are collected at home, evidently belong to a people who are clothed in "fine linen" every day.'

In 1835 an official inquiry into the paper duty was held by a Parliamentary Commission. John Dickinson gave evidence before the Commissioners, but when they came to cross-examine

[1] Monthly supplement of the *Penny Magazine*, 31 August 1833.

him he grew so infuriated by their stupidity that after swearing under his breath for some minutes he clapped on his hat and rushed out into Westminster Hall.

In 1837 the duty was reduced to $1\frac{1}{2}$d. a lb. On 1 May Ann thankfully entered in her diary: 'We have had many perceptible blessings shower'd on us this week. My beloved husband . . . has heard he will have half the Duty off his Papers, which will considerably lighten his burthens, and has put him in good spirits.' In 1839, however, the laws for the exaction of the duty were clarified and made more severe, with the imposition of copious and heavy penalties for every infringement, with or without fraudulent intention. The reduction of the duty was a great stimulus to trade; in 1840 no fewer than 280 machines were at work in the Kingdom, making 1,600 miles of paper a day, and the price was nearly halved.

Agitation against the duty none the less continued; Ann Dickinson tells us on 19 December 1844: 'Mr. D. got thro' his speech well at meeting for the abolition of Paper duty.' The duty, however, remained in force for seventeen years more.

The Act of 1837 abolished the Excise duty on stained paper. Some three years later Dickinson began to develop the manufacture of coated coloured papers at Home Park. The work was done by hand, sheet by sheet. There was a steady demand for it for packing by lace and linen manufacturers, and in 1842 a branch for its sale was set up at Nottingham, to be followed a few years later by one at Belfast. These also sold the cards for use in Jacquard looms, and the boards round which lace and linen were packed for sale.

The main staple of manufacture, however, continued to be paper for books. In 1838 Dickinson publicly stated[1] that his business lay more in printing-paper than in writing-paper. The accounts of 1842 show an increase in the number of publishers on the books: the Clarendon Press, the S.P.C.K., Bradbury and

[1] Commission on the Post Office, 2 March, answer 2491.

Evans, Blackie & Son, Moxon, Sampson Low, Samuel Bagster and Bohn among them. By the next year, Simpkins and Chambers were added, as well as such institutions and societies as the Anti-Slavery Society, the English Historical Society, and the British Museum.

Competition in the printing field was growing as the publishers began to exploit the demand for cheap books.[1] In April 1852 Dickinson wrote[2] to his partner: 'Combe has been here to-day wanting cheaper paper for inferior books to compete with the Scotch. Their Pearl Bible weighs half a pound and they sell it for 6d. The Scotch have a common thin deprinted thing at 5d. and this annoys the B[ible] Society. What cutting!'

Dickinson's own interests at this time were centred on the question of sizing. In 1839 he patented[3] a method of tub-sizing paper that had already been engine-sized, to improve its strength and non-absorbent quality. The size and paper are placed in a closed steam-heated cylinder, from which air is abstracted to cause bubbles to form in the size. In 1840[4] he patented a process of continuous tub-sizing, by which dried paper is unwound from a reel to pass over guide rolls into heated size at the bottom of a container, the excess being removed by passage between a pair of press rolls.

The scale of Dickinson's operations may be judged (having regard to the contemporary scale of wages) by his wage sheets for January 1837. At Apsley they averaged £47 10s. a week; at Nash, £42; at Home Park £39; at Croxley, £52 10s.; and at Batchworth, £90. Apsley produced 815 reams a week, Nash 860, Home Park 910, Croxley 1,445; Batchworth had an output of 36 tons of half-stuff.

[1] There was a Spottiswoode crash in 1846, but Dickinson got clear of his connexions with the firm some months before.

[2] J.D.E.

[3] Patent No. 8242, Section 5, 17 October 1839.

[4] Patent No. 8751, 23 December 1840. Machinery on the lines of the patent was set up at Apsley in 1848 in a new building.

By 1838 Nash Mills were making about eight tons of paper a week. In 1840 John Dickinson set up an engineering department there, to serve all his mills, under the charge of Leonard Stephenson, who had, about 1825, been the first apprentice of the great George Stephenson at his Sheldon Works near Darlington.[1] He worked with Robert Stephenson in East Anglia and at Derby. In 1840 he was working on the London and Birmingham Railway at Watford. He came to Dickinson's notice, and was appointed engineer in charge of all machinery and boiler plant in all the mills. He found his millwrights 'lazy, drunken good-for-nowts', and brought in his own men. His appointment inaugurated a time of reorganization of the engineering side of the Mills, that was to do much to get over the difficulty of variable and inadequate water-power.

He did not always find Dickinson reasonable to work with. In 1843, for example, Dickinson wished to build a new office for the Stationery Department at Apsley. Stephenson came up there with him and they planned the building together. Dickinson indicated the plan by stepping it out in both directions and making a hole at the corners with his stick. Stephenson ventured to point out that the scheme was not in line with the Beam Engine House, which it adjoined. 'In line be damned, Stephenson', retorted his master. 'Where I have marked it out, there it is to be.' And so it was, out of line and square.[2]

---

[1] See a report from his great-nephew, Mr. W. Stephenson, made to the firm in November 1930. I had the pleasure as a child of knowing Mr. Stephenson, then an old man living at No. 1 Nash Mills. He died in 1905 at the age of ninety-four.

[2] Reminiscences of Mr. W. Stephenson. The building was later demolished to make room for the new Envelope Building.

VI

STAMPS AND ENVELOPES

1837–1857

THE development of the trade in paper to correspond with the immense increase in its manufacture was hampered not only by the duties on paper and rags but also by an archaic postal system. A uniform rate of twopence a letter had been instituted for London in 1801, but outside the Metropolitan area there were fantastic variations in postage. The amount due had to be ascertained and marked on every packet; postmasters had to keep elaborate accounts and be debited with any unpaid postage; and all letters had to be paid for by the recipient. It cost 8d. to send a letter (that is, a single sheet of paper weighing less than an ounce) from London to Brighton; 1s. 1½d. from London to Edinburgh; 1s. 4d. from London to Belfast. The rate was based on mileage, running from 4d. for a distance under 15 miles to 1s. between 230 and 300 miles, with an extra ½d. in Scotland. The regulations of the service had been codified in 1808, before the days of railways, and when mechanically made paper was still an inventor's dream.

Rowland Hill, the son of a schoolmaster who had worked out a system of stenography, was himself a schoolmaster of a progressive kind, who had invented a rotary printing-press which could not be used because of the way in which paper duty was levied on the sheet.[1] In 1835 he was appointed Secretary to the South Australian Commission and learned something of the ways in which public opinion could be influenced and legislation

[1] See p. 65.

initiated. In 1837 he published a pamphlet entitled *Post Office Reform*, that pointed out that over the past twenty years the population of Great Britain had increased by some six million, but that the postal revenue had shown a slight diminution. After exhaustive analyses of the costs which the fee covered, he recommended a flat rate of one penny for each half ounce for letters posted and delivered in the United Kingdom, with an additional charge of a penny for each additional half ounce, up to a convenient limit, for heavier packets. In his view this charge, on the greater number of letters and packets that it would encourage, would more than cover the cost of the service to the Post Office. He further suggested the sale of stamped covers to the public, to permit of the prepayment of letters.[1]

In 1838 petitions on the subject poured into the House of Commons, and a Select Committee was in due course appointed. John Dickinson was conscious that its decisions might greatly affect his fortunes.[2] The paper which he had invented in 1828[3] and patented in 1829,[4] with threads of silk incorporated into it, had been used since about 1829 for Exchequer Bonds and for other Government documents which required authentication. It was made at Nash Mills behind locked doors on two machines constantly watched by excisemen. The threads had to be laid at an equal distance from each other, and mended when they broke: a task entrusted to two trustworthy women.

Dickinson's interest in Rowland Hill's proposed reforms lay

[1] In the *Companion to the Newspaper* of 1 June 1874 Charles Knight had suggested stamped covers, but only for newspapers. See Rowland Hill and George Birkbeck Hill, *Life of Sir Rowland Hill*, 1880, 1, p. 218.
Adhesive postage stamps had been suggested apparently as early as 1834 by James Chalmers of Arbroath.
[2] Fanny records on 27 February 1838: 'Pa went to drink tea at Rowland Hill's.'
[3] Ann Dickinson's diary, 16 September 1828.
[4] See p. 43.

in the stamped covers. Letters at this time, as long before, consisted in a single sheet of paper folded on itself so that the message was inside and the outside was plain for the address. They were sealed by a wafer or a wax seal impressed with a signet. By 1835 'pockets' or 'envelopes' were already coming into fashion.[1] On 13 March 1835 Fanny Dickinson wrote to her brother at Eton 'on blue notepaper enclosed in a *pocket*', and on 6 April 1836 she was busy 'making envelopes all day' to send out invitations to a party. By July 1837 she was noting on the fly-leaf of her diary: 'Envelopes at 2/6 per 100, to be had at 209 Regent Street.' These seem to have been sold flat and ungummed; the four corners met under the seal. John Dickinson astutely conceived the plan that the official stamped envelopes or covers should be made of his thread paper.

Rowland Hill was examined before the Commission on 13 February 1838 and proposed, as he had done in his pamphlet, that there should be a penny post; that there should be hourly deliveries in London; that district post offices should be set up, and that the two staffs of letter-carriers then employed, local and general, should be merged into one service of postmen. He made the sensible suggestion that these plans should first be tried out in the London district.

He had already suggested the use of stamped covers in a letter to the Chancellor of the Exchequer[2] and now repeated the suggestion. 'Let stamped covers or sheets of paper be supplied to the public from the Stamp Office or Post Office, as may be most convenient and sold at such a price as to include the postage . . . Covers, at various prices, would be required for packets of various weights; and each stamp should have the weight it is entitled to carry legibly printed with the stamp.'

[1] They had occasionally been used in France in the seventeenth century. The word occurs (according to the O.E.D.) in English in 1714 and 1735; it then probably indicated a simple covering sheet.
[2] *Life of Rowland Hill*, 1, p. 270.

He also tentatively suggested the use of 'a bit of paper just large enough to bear the stamp, and covered at the back with a glutinous wash', to be stuck on letters which had to be re-addressed.

He was asked:[1] 'Would you propose that all stamped letter-paper should be supplied by the Stamp department?', and replied, 'That is not essential to the plan; it might, or it might not, according as the public convenience, or the wishes of the public, might be best consulted: my own idea is, that a peculiar paper—I will take Dickinson's for example—a paper which has lines of thread or silk stretched through its substance, and apparent on each surface, is the best preventive of forgery I have seen; and I should propose that the public should have their option, either buying such paper stamped at the Stamp-office, or that they might send in their own paper to be stamped, there could then be no charge of monopoly made against the Government; but I think it very likely that the public would prefer the paper issued from the Stamp-office, and it certainly would be a convenience to the Post Office if that were the case, because the risk of forgery being so much diminished by the use of such a paper as Dickinson's, the duty of the inspector would be very much diminished, and I think all prospect of loss to the revenue from forgery would be at an end.'

Mr. Thorneley, one of the Commissioners, continued the questions.[2] 'Could the supply to the country be so managed as not to be considered monopoly by the paper-manufacturers?' —'I think it might be managed in this way, that the Government should give parties the option of either purchasing their stamped paper at Somerset house, or of sending in their own paper to be stamped; if that plan were adopted, I should then recommend that the Government should use Dickinson's paper; and I think that the advantages of that paper would be so great,

[1] *Report of Commission*, 2129.
[2] *Ibid*, 2143.

supposing that we could sell it at the same price to the public at which other paper was sold, or at a very small difference, that the stationers themselves would very soon come to us for it, and that the imputation of monopoly would be completely avoided.'

Another Commissioner, Mr. Chalmers, inquired:[1] 'Is it your plan, if you use Dickinson's paper for these stamped covers, to limit the sale by Mr. Dickinson of that paper to Government?' —'Certainly, because that in itself would constitute a very material obstacle to forgery.'

'Would that not give rise to complaints of monopoly on the part of other paper-makers?'—'I think not; if the Government could enter into a contract with Mr. Dickinson to supply them with such paper as they might want, giving any stationer in the kingdom or any individual, the privilege of bringing whatever paper he chose, of whatever quality or price, to be stamped, there could be no complaint I should think, of monopoly.' . . .

'Do you propose to stamp whole sheets of Mr. Dickinson's paper, or to limit it to covers?'—'I take it, the duty of the Stamp-office would be to stamp pieces of papers of any size, whether half-sheets or whole-sheets; it would be the province of the stationer to manufacture them into envelopes if the customers demanded them, and for which he would make whatever charge he could agree upon with his customers.'

Rowland Hill was then interrogated[2] on the question of stamps. 'Are you to be understood to express an unfavourable opinion of a separate stamp to be affixed as a label?'—'Yes, I think that would be found inconvenient, inasmuch as it would be very apt to rub off; but it has occurred to us that both might be used. For instance, if it were thought expedient that the kind of label which is now called a medicine label,[3] and which is printed by machinery at Somerset-house, should be printed on

[1] *Ibid.*, 2162, 2163, 2169.
[2] *Ibid.*, 2215.
[3] That is, the Government label attached to patent medicines.

Dickinson's paper, the cost of the paper itself would be very small, not an element worth taking into calculation; this sheet of paper (showing one) would hold at least one-third more stamps than it does now, consequently the expense of the paper would be nothing, and these might be used by pasting them on the outside cover of a letter. The difficulty of impressing a single stamp of this sort (the medicine stamp) on half-sheets of paper, is that we must damp all the paper, and it would require great space of do so, and it would injure it for writing on. It must be hot-pressed probably before it could be written upon, for the water would take out the size.'

Dickinson was in his turn examined on 2 March.[1] He had already, in 1830, designed and had printed a pair of demonstration letter-sheets to show how the idea could be put into use, and had circulated them through the stationery trade. These were made in the style of a banknote, with elaborate 'engine turned' ornament. Much of his evidence was taken up by an account of his thread-paper, its manufacture, and the difficulties of forging it. He spoke warmly in favour of its use both for stamped covers and for adhesive stamps. He considered that it would be possible to manufacture a gross of stamped envelopes for about a shilling, if the excise duty were remitted, but refused to make an estimate of a similar quantity on ordinary paper. He recognized that one of the difficulties that lay in the adoption of stamped covers of any kind was the attitude of the Excise to them, since as Government products they would probably be exempt from duty and in a small degree tend to diminish the consumption of paper on which duty was levied, and suggested various ways by which the loss to the Excise might be made good. The questions of distribution and monopoly were considered at length. He was in favour of producing stamped covers of one size only, and of cutting out the central part and using it as a label for packets too large to go in the cover of standard size,

[1] *Report of Commission*, 2388–2505.

75

which he thought should be nine inches by seven and three-eighths.

A Mercantile Committee was set up to promote the uniform penny postage; most of the publishers, paper-makers and stationers subscribed to its funds. The two latter favoured adhesive stamps rather than covers, for they feared a monopoly of Dickinson thread paper. Dickinson, with an acute sense of what constituted publicity, had the number of the *Athenæum* for 28 April 1838 containing a review of the evidence on the subject, printed in part on his thread paper.

The Commission in due course recommended the optional use of stamped penny covers within the London district. The Government assented in principle, but in fact did nothing, beyond passing a new Post Office Act that codified all the previous legislation. After many petitions had been presented in the House of Commons a Select Committee was finally appointed[1] in November. They reported in favour of a low uniform rate, and on 15 December the Chancellor of the Exchequer announced that stamped covers would be introduced.

In June 1839 Lord John Russell announced to the House that the Government would propose a Resolution in favour of a uniform penny postage. This measure formed part of the Budget proposed by the Chancellor of the Exchequer on 5 July. Shortly afterwards he received a deputation of stationers who had come to say that they would be inconvenienced by the issue of Government stamped envelopes.

The debates were followed with great interest by John Dickinson. On 13 July Fanny tells us: 'Dr. Pa' came down pr. early train dogtired having been at the House all night.' The measure was finally passed on 17 August. On 23 August the Lords of the Treasury issued a proclamation inviting 'all

[1] John Dickinson was clearly anxious. His daughter's diary for 1 November 1839 records: 'Pa came down late—bad news about P.O. covers.'

artists, men of science, and the public in general' to offer proposals within the next three months 'as to the manner in which the stamp may best be brought into use', with prizes of £200 and £100 for the best suggestions.

John Dickinson spent the three months of respite in improving the mechanism of his thread paper, to allow of the more exact placing of the silk thread in two or more layers, a certain number near one face of the sheet and others nearer the back, by fixing bobbins so that threads touched the 'making cylinder' in definite places under control. He patented the new device in October[1] together with the design of a sizing machine heated by steam under pressure.

More than 2,500 entries were received for the Government competition. It was won by William Mulready, a Royal Academician of fifty-two, who recommended an envelope, to be sold flat and ungummed, with an elaborate engraved design to prevent forgery. In December he was invited to submit his final drawing for it; this was engraved by John Thompson and printed by William Clowes and Co. on Dickinson thread paper. On 26 February 1840 Harriet returned from a gay visit to her grandmother at Woolwich to Bedford Row to find her father torn between anxiety for his son, who was ill in Germany, 'and joy, the latter at securing the grant for P.O. covers, for which thank God!' He spent the next evening 'scheming about making types'. A special thread paper was devised with one blue thread between two red, the red nearer the reverse and the blue nearer the printing surface of the paper. On 19 March Dickinson took his daughters 'to see the envelope paper making'. The first proofs were submitted to the Queen on 3 April 1840 and were formally approved at the end of the month. They were first issued on 6 May. On 3 May John Evans, newly arrived at Nash Mills, wrote to his mother: 'There are two machines making paper for

[1] 17 October 1839, Patent No. 8242.

the envelopes and stamps of two different patterns. There are three excisemen always there to look after the paper.'

William Mulready was a painter of great technical competence, who excelled in such *genre* pictures as his 'Choosing the Wedding Gown'. As a designer in line he was less gifted, and from their first appearance his envelopes were a target for criticism. Leech caricatured them in *Punch*. A London daily paper[1] described them. 'In the centre, at the top, sits Britannia, throwing out her arms, as if in a tempest of fury, at four winged urchins, intended to represent post-boys, letter-carriers, or Mercuries, but who, instead of making use of their wings and flying, appear in the act of striking out or swimming, which would have been natural enough if they had been furnished with fins instead of wings. On the right of Britannia there are a brace of elephants, all packed and ready to start, when some Hindoo, Chinese, Arabic, or Turkish Merchants, standing quietly by, have closed their bargains and correspondence. The elephants are symbolic of the lightness and rapidity with which Mr. Rowland Hill's penny post is to be carried on, and perhaps, also, of the power requisite for transporting the £1,500 a-year to his quarters which is all he obtains for strutting about the Post Office, with his hands in his pockets, and nothing to do like a fish out of water. On the left of Britannia, who looks herself very much like a termagant, there is an agglomeration of native Indians, Missionaries, Yankees, and casks of tobacco, with a sprinkling of foliage, and the rotten stem of a tree, not forgetting a little terrier dog inquisitively gliding between the legs of the mysterious conclave to see the row. Below, on the left, a couple of heads of the damsel tribe are curiously peering over a valentine just received (scene, Valentine's Day), whilst a little girl is pressing the elders for a sight of Cupid, and the heart transfixed with a score of arrows. On the right again stands a dutiful boy reading to his anxious mamma an account of her husband's hapless shipwreck,

[1] Quoted, *Life of Rowland Hill*, I, p. 393.

who, with hands clasped, is blessing Rowland Hill for the cheap rate at which she gets the disastrous intelligence. At the bottom of all there is the word "Postage", done in small upon a large pattern of filagree work. With very great propriety the name of the artist is conspicuously placed in one corner, so that the public and posterity may know who is the worthy Oliver of the genius of a Rowland on this triumphant occasion. As may well be imagined, it is no common man, for the mighty effort has taxed the powers of the Royal Academy itself, if the engraved announcement of Mr. Mulready, R.A., in the corner may be credited . . .'

Hill, in fact, was not popular. He had been put in, under the Treasury, to organize the Post Office, and soon found himself in conflict with vested interests and established officers. Moreover, since the Mulready envelope had been introduced by the Whigs, it was assured of Tory opposition. Even had Mulready been a greater designer, it is doubtful whether his envelope would have been a great success. As it was, it had a life of little more than six months,[1] though it established an agreeable tradition of decorated envelopes, that flourished for a few years, until their use was discouraged by Post Office regulations. It was not out of Mulready envelopes that the firm of John Dickinson achieved success.

The parliamentary implementation of Rowland Hill's proposals included not only specially printed 'covers', but also adhesive stamps, though his own view had been that these would prove less satisfactory. The competitions organized by the Government included one with a prize of £500 for such stamps, which was awarded to Frederick Heath's design of the Queen's

---

[1] *The Life of Rowland Hill*, I, p. 395, says 'that the public rejection of the Mulready envelope was so complete as to necessitate the destruction of nearly all the vast number prepared for issue. It is a curious fact that a machine had to be constructed for the purpose; the attempt to do the work by fire in closed stoves (fear of robbery forbade the use of open ones) having absolutely failed.'

head now universally known as the 'penny black'.[1] This was on sale, like the Mulready envelopes, on 6 May 1840 and like it was experimentally printed on Dickinson thread paper, as were the later Penny Red and Twopenny Blue, and the embossed 1s. and 10d. octagonal stamps.[2]

Early in 1841 it was suggested that stamped envelopes should take the place of the obsolete Mulreadys, the stamp being embossed on the right-hand top corner of a plain envelope. At first it was proposed that Dickinson thread paper should be used, but a letter from Rowland Hill to John Dickinson of 26 February 1841[3] indicates that the proposed cost of rather more than 2s. a lb. 'is so much higher than the present cost, even including that of Excise superintendence, that unless you can make a very considerable reduction in the price it is useless to consider the question further'.

In fact Hill had, for family reasons, joined the party that was opposed to the Dickinson monopoly. On 19 February 1852[4] John Dickinson wrote to his partner:

'There is rather an ugly move at the Stamp Office. I have been with Mr. Thornton (Deputy Chairman) to-day . . . and there I found an overwhelming mass of complaints of papers cut by blue thread and I found the Board thoroughly indoctrinated by Hill with the notion that the threads must be abolished and the water mark substituted.

'I could barely get a reprieve for trying the present 300 Rms.

'It appears that enormous quantities are spoiled in stamping and it is made [to] appear that the thread paper is quite objectionable.[5]

[1] The Mulready 1d. envelope was printed in black, and the 2d. in blue, and the same colour scheme was used for the stamps. The embossed stamps were made from a die designed by the medallist Wyon.

[2] The first Bavarian stamps, produced in 1849, were also printed on paper with silk threads in it.

[3] In the author's possession.   [4] J.D.E.

[5] The thread paper could, in fact, only be used satisfactorily for imperforate stamps; when perforation was introduced it was found that the threads got entangled in the pins of the perforating-machine.

'Now are we to fight for the whole thing, making envelopes and all? or try what can be done by making the paper a little stronger and thicker and with *silk* blue thread? Or are we to try to get a good price for water mark paper?

'I am for the 2nd. of these proposals because I think if we can get over the difficulty we keep the stronger hold on the job. It is a choice of evils . . .'

The Treasury officials, however, still felt that the thread paper was the best protection against forgery, and it continued to be used for a few years for Post Office envelopes as well as for Exchequer Bills. On 11 April 1852 John Dickinson could write to his partner: 'I think I have turned aside this scheme for water mark envelopes, but am glad it did not emanate from the Mills.'

In May 1859, however, John Evans was writing to his cousin Fanny Phelps in Madeira:[1] 'I am rather bothered just now at our losing the supply of the Paper for Postage Envs. They are for giving up the thread altogether and are trying to throw the whole affair into Delarue's hands, but I think they will find they have made a mistake . . .' Shortly afterwards the threads were omitted, and the Post Office envelopes became not a Dickinson but a De la Rue monopoly.[2]

The possibility of using adhesive stamps on plain envelopes, and the demise of the Mulready covers made an immense difference to the business of every paper-maker and stationer in the Kingdom. The economics of Rowland Hill's reforms were based on the assumption that a low and uniform rate of postage within the United Kingdom would result in an enormous increase in the number of letters sent. The assumption was valid; between 1840 and 1842 the chargeable letters in the United Kingdom increased from about 75,000,000 to 196,000,000, and the gross revenue rose to about 63 per cent of that of the former fantastic charges. By 1849 nearly

[1] J.D.E.

[2] I have several forgeries of these made by John Evans to show that they were easily imitated.

329,000,000 postage paid letters were posted. Since all these were enclosed in envelopes, some Post Office ones with embossed stamps, still more plain envelopes with adhesive stamps, they represented an immense new trade.[1]

It was the men with the closest business associations with the new postal service who first saw the possibilities of exploiting it. Up to now the relatively small numbers of envelopes required had been made by a simple guillotine cutter and sold flat, to be folded and gummed by hand by the retailer or his client and finally closed by a wafer or a seal.[2] On 15 December 1840,[3] Rowland Hill first saw in the room which his brother Edwin occupied at Somerset House, in virtue of the office of Supervisor of Stamps to which he had just been appointed, the earliest model of an envelope machine which he had invented, which was not yet practicable. He developed it in association with Warren de la Rue,[4] a retail paper-merchant of an inventive turn of mind. On 17 March 1845 it was sufficiently far advanced to be patented.[5] It provided not only for cutting the envelopes by machinery, but also for folding them mechanically, by an inverted box which descended over the blank. It needed two operators, one to feed and one to take off, and was estimated to produce some eighteen or nineteen thousand envelopes a day, not gummed. By 1850 they were producing gummed envelopes. By 1851 they had eleven machines at work.

A second envelope machine was patented by Amédée François

[1] Ann Dickinson records in her diary for 7 April 1847: 'A good acct. of the Mills above 2400 rms. wk. on the average of this Qr.'

[2] An envelope produced by Henry Tuck in 1840 was intended to be closed by the postage stamp, but Postal Regulations soon forbade this.

[3] *Life of Rowland Hill*, 1, p. 418.

[4] On 1 December 1846, John Dickinson entertained Warren de la Rue at a men's party with the Blackwoods.

[5] Patent No. 10,565.

Rémond in 1849 and 1850.[1] In it envelope blanks were placed in a pile on an adjustable platform and were fed forward one by one by means of two hollow moving fingers or aspirators, each having an opening on the underside communicating by means of a flexible tube with an air-pump or bellows. On exhausting the air, one of the fingers picked up a blank, moved forward and placed it over a die, in a rectangular box or recess with perforated sides and bottom. A rectangular plunger descended, pushed down the blank to the bottom of the box and in so doing raised the flaps of the envelope at right angles. The plunger withdrew, leaving the blank in the box. Air was forced in through side perforations to 'push' or incline the flaps inwards. Again the plunger descended, this time completing the folding, some inner projections on the plunger causing the flaps to fold over in correct sequence. The die or box had a hinged bottom which now opened, and the folded envelope fell out. Automatic gumming was provided by a gum-covered surface so placed that when the blank was passing from the pile to the box it picked up the gum. Rémond's second patent[2] arranged for the dusting of the flap with powdered gum, the flap having already been automatically wetted in the machine. It was estimated[3] that it could produce forty envelopes, gummed, embossed, and ready for sealing, in a minute.

John Dickinson had early been interested in Rémond's machine, but recognized that it needed much further development before it could be used commercially. He determined to buy it. On 19 December 1850 Fanny tells us 'the experiment with the Envelope machine . . . was *almost* successful, so the purchasers compromised the matter for £250'. Dickinson realized that his production was not equal to the demand. On 28 January 1852 he wrote to his partner Charles Longman:

[1] Patent No. 12,493, 28 February 1849.
[2] Patent No. 13036, 15 April 1850.
[3] *Illustrated London News*, 5 July 1851.

'We have been getting behind in our London deliveries of Envelopes. I have been insisting on their staying till 8 o'clock to-night and that the new Clerk should be here every morning by 8.'

Meanwhile John Evans was at work improving the details of the Rémond machine. The envelopes first produced by it were unsatisfactory. On 8 March 1852 Dickinson wrote to Charles Longman: 'I have seen young Penny to-day and he considers that he has done well this year with Envelopes, but he says the first we sent were so wretchedly bad that they damp'd the sale. He goes off on Monday and wants better samples.'[1]

Dickinson's mills were soon turning out great quantities of envelopes, and the partners were beginning to consider undercutting prices. A letter from Evans to Charles Longman[2] declares that their envelopes are cheaper 'than Stockens, Rodriguez or any advertized firm's. But suppose, notwithstanding these reasons for an increased sale, the average of 1840 to 1846 were doubled only instead of trebled, yet the profit accruing from 640,000 pr. wk. at 4/- would be superior to that from 960,000 pr. week at 3/7½ . . .'

'It is likewise to be considered whether the causing of envelopes to be retailed at less than the regular wholesale price would not set the Stationers against us and materially interfere with the common Envelope Trade.'

The question of costs had taken on a new urgency. For many years after 1848 John Evans was engaged in making detailed estimates, from raw materials to the finished article, on which selling prices for paper of every kind could be based. At the same time he was making many trials, in collaboration with

---

[1] J.D.E. On 1 April he wrote from London: 'I am sorry to say there are some fellows from the North selling Envelopes very cheap. They are not bad and are not stamped and cemented but they do us much mischief.'

[2] J.D.E. not dated; apparently about 1848.

Ann Dickinson's engineer nephew J. W. Grover, in the experimental manufacture of half-stuff from different kinds of unsorted and low grade rags, especially cotton, and in designing details of machines to deal with them.[1]

It came as a great shock to the firm when in 1856 De la Rue's —who had bought up Edwin Hill's interest in the rival envelope machine—tried to get an injunction against Dickinson's for infringement of their patent, especially in the matter of the actual folding of envelopes, on the ground that the principle was the same and only details of the mechanism different.[2]

De la Rue's first attempt was a failure. Fanny proudly wrote in her diary, on 3 December 1856, 'The good news of Delarue's defeat in his Motion for an injunction against *our Firm* to prevent their using the machine for making envelopes—dismissed even without hearing the Deft's. Counsel. A great triumph!'

De la Rue's returned to the fray, and brought an action in Chancery against the firm of John Dickinson and Co. On 14 February 1857 Fanny entered in her diary the news of 'an adverse verdict on *every* point—and a most unjust one too—the jury and the judge were evidently entirely against them from the very first. Poor dear Papa, what a blow for him!' The next day she tells us: 'I walked off . . . to Brook St. and saw the poor old people in great dismay and indignation of course, but Pa much too pugnacious, I fear. He went off in a great puff to Mulready's . . .' Fanny Phelps was staying with the Dickinsons, and wrote to Harriet:[3] 'Jack said directly on Saturday that there was no redress . . . The uncle seems not to mind about the money, but poor dear he does care dreadfully about the

[1] See letter from J. W. Grover, 8 December 1848. J.D.E.

[2] The patent law had recently been changed under the Patent Act of 1848.

On 19 December 1849, Warren de la Rue had taken out a further patent (No. 12,904) for improvements in the manufacture of envelopes, notably in gumming and pressing.

[3] J.D.E.

imputation and he is so annoyed because Delarue has been boasting about London, naturally enough, that he has "beat Dickinson" . . . These hard envelope times . . . What will become of the 400 people at work on them?'

Certain points of law arising out of the specifications remained to be tried. On 25 May Fanny wrote: 'This morning up very early . . . To Westminster Hall . . . in the brougham . . . found me in a very comfortable gallery in the Court of Queen's Bench with my basket of *stores* and work and there I remained all day till past 4, listening to the Cause of Delarue and Dickinson wh. was opened . . . at 11.30 by Sir Fred. Thesiger in a pleasant but not very pithy speech of 2 hours. He was followed by Mr. Grove etc. till 3 when Serjeant Byles began his reply on our side, and kept on till 4 when the Court rose. There were 4 judges *in Banco*, Lord Campbell (who was evidently bias'd all thro' in Delarue's favor), Coleridge (who is Campbell's echo) Erle and Crompton, who unfortunately left before our case began.' The next day she was there again. 'When [our case] was called Serjt. Byles was absent and the case was argued by Hugh Hill (in a dull speech) Bovill (in an admirable manner) and Webster (only soso). It was evident as yesterday that Campbell was completely against us, and at 2.30 Byles having returned and the other Counsel finished, he declined saying anything, so the case terminated, and the judges after cogitating for a few minutes said they wd. defer their judgement, but there is but little doubt what their decision will be, alas!' The next day she had to go 'to Brook St. Saw Ma and told her the sad news I had just heard . . . that the judgement had been given this morning and *against* us!!' On 12 June the Chancery injunction to restrain the firm from using their machines came up, and was in part successful. On 16 June 1857 a financial settlement with De la Rue's was effected, rather against John Dickinson's will, and Fanny could write in her diary: 'Thank Heaven!'

VII

THE FAMILY BUSINESS
1850–1857

FANNY DICKINSON made a great success of her marriage
to Frederick Pratt Barlow. He was the kindest, quietest and
gentlest of men, with a clear brain, a good legal training,
and a great respect for his wife's capabilities. She was handsome,
vigorous, with plenty of *joie de vivre*, the Dickinson temper
that got her into constant trouble with her cooks, and the
Dickinson competence in practical affairs, that in spite of her
temper made her an admirable housewife. She had few intellectual interests: for her, literature was French novels (which at
least she read in the original), music the Covent Garden Opera,
and art the Royal Academy. She was, indeed, the most normal
and conventional of women; yet with a love for her family and
a certain *entrain*—a Brissac quality which no English word will
translate—that made a conventional life a feat of creative style.
She was a social climber, in a perfectly amiable way. John Evans
(whom she despised as unfashionable and rather priggishly
learned) none the less wrote of her:[1] 'I am one of those who
think there is a great deal to like in Fanny B. though she can
be hard at times and has a position to maintain and does it.'

The slightly precarious nature of the position she maintained
is exemplified by her endeavours to put a good face on things.
She had her own brougham, sociable, footman and liveries, but
jobbed both her coachman and her horses; she had her own
cottage piano, but hired a grand from Collard's for the two

[1] Letter to Fanny Phelps, 1859. J.D.E.

87

months of the London season when she gave her grand dinner parties; she always spent the proper months from July to October in the country, but in a furnished house. None the less she remained a complete townswoman; her idea of a garden was a conservatory, with 'delicious' tiles from Minton's; her notion of a country expedition was a drive in the lanes of Brompton, Fulham and Putney. She was never happier than when enjoying a family holiday in a furnished house at Brighton.

There can be no doubt that she played her part in the development of the firm by her social activities. She entertained in her grand house in Rutland Gate[1] not only her neighbours and her more aristocratic acquaintances, but also publishers such as Longmans and Ormes and Rees's, authors ranging from Martin Tupper to Froude and Disraeli, and journalists such as Delane, Dasent, Forster and Russell, the *Times* correspondent in the Crimea. Her great occupation, once she had arranged for her family's comfort and well-being, was paying and receiving calls. It is pleasant to see in her diaries how her love for her husband and her seven children (one died soon after birth) turned what might have been merely an ambitious woman of the world into a fine and unselfish character.

Her sister, Harriet, was very different from Fanny, though a strong sisterly affection existed between the two. She was far more sensitive and far less conventional; much less concerned with getting on in life, and much more genuinely intellectual and artistic. Her girlhood was clouded, as her sister's had not been, by the claims of her mother's ill-health; she minded her father's hot temper and rough manners far more than her sister did. Her looks were less showy, her social aplomb quieter; she judged things by a different and more spiritual scale of values. Her quiet life at Abbot's Hill threw her much into the company of John Evans, who often came up to make a fourth at whist or

---

[1] In 1848 they moved to a larger house, 26 Rutland Gate, where later they built a ballroom.

to report on the mills to his uncle. None the less it came as a surprise to everyone when in 1848 they declared their intention of marriage.[1] John Dickinson was furious; he did not want to lose his daughter, and if he had to, he wished her to make a match with a man of wealth and position. John Evans was doing well in the mills, but he had no fortune, and was a poor parson's son. None the less the steadfast purpose of the young people was too much for him, and they married on 12 September 1850. Fanny Pratt Barlow strongly disapproved, and though at the wedding she was favourably impressed by 'Mama's superb violet and black silk dress, with 1st. rate pink bonnet', and Mrs. Charles Longman's 'beautiful pink bonnet from Paris and new silk cloak', she found her Evans cousins 'very ordinary' and decided that 'dear old Fred beat [the bridegroom] hollow with his new blue long stock and white waistcoat and handsome face'.

Harriet did not enter upon matrimony with the brilliant worldly hopes that Fanny had enjoyed. 'Our prospects', she wrote[2] to John Evans not long before their marriage, 'are not very bright but let us look them boldly in the face. They do not promise us much. We shall I fear never be rich and never be independent; but still if it please God to bless us I hope we may be happy.'

Happy they were, even though they had to live in the little Red House by the gate to Nash Mills. Harriet's work lay less in entertaining than in helping her village neighbours. Before 1855 she had started a library for Nash Mills, and had set up a school for the village girls in a derelict chapel. The teacher had been trained for three weeks at the Westminster Training School; she was paid £10 a year, with 2d. a week from each pupil. Harriet herself tried to be in the school to help her for a little time each day. John Evans started a boys' school at Frogmore End, with some financial help from the firm.

[1] I have told the story more fully in *Time and Chance*, p. 74 *et sqq.*
[2] J.D.E.

In 1853 Charles Longman, who had inherited a large fortune from his father,[1] bought the Shendish estate on the western side of the valley, and proceeded to build a fine house there, so that in 1856 the Evanses were able to move into Nash House, where Harriet had been born. She already had three sons, Arthur, Lewis and Norman, and soon after her return to Nash House her first daughter was born. A second daughter was born in December 1857, but Harriet fell ill and died on New Year's morning.

It was a tragic time for John Evans; yet, with five mills and five children under seven to look after, he could not remain solitary. In July 1859 he married as his second wife his cousin, Fanny Phelps. She had no children of her own, but did everything to make Nash House as happy a home as it could be for a man haunted by the memory of his first love. Dickinson might not approve of his nephew as a son-in-law, but he recognized his good brain, his inventive capacity, and his power of dealing with figures and calculations of every kind. At the end of 1850 he admitted both his sons-in-law to partnership in his firm. It was a sensible move, since it was quite clear that his own son had not the stability of character for a business career. Fred Pratt Barlow dissolved his partnership with Justin, ceased to be a practising solicitor, and spent the working week in the Dickinson office in the Old Bailey. John Evans took over more and more responsibility in the actual running of the mills and their machinery. He was by far the more brilliant of the two, but he appreciated Frederick's integrity, good sense and quiet friendliness, and the two younger partners often found themselves in tacit alliance to circumvent their father-in-law's dictatorial ways.

Fred Barlow's help was particularly valuable to Dickinson at this time, for he was engaged in a good deal of litigation, and

[1] The publishing firm, after Thomas Norton Longman's death in 1842, was controlled by his other sons Thomas and William. The latter married Fred Pratt Barlow's sister Emma.

not only with De la Rue. The perennial trouble with the Grand Junction Canal continued, in spite of the settlement of 1818. The question of short water led John Dickinson into scientific inquiries, in which his other nephew helped him. Soon after 1840 he made a percolation rain-gauge on the principles of Dr. Dalton, to determine, by the measuring of the rain that fell in the winter, what amount of water would be flowing in the Gade during the next summer's short-water season. If twelve or fourteen inches of the rain that fell in the water passed through the three feet of soil in the gauge, he could reckon on a full river in the summer; if only three or four inches passed, he could plan to meet the exigencies of a 'short-water' time. On 19 November 1849 Fanny tells us: 'Papa, J. Evans and Harriet worked hard to complete a geological Map (begun last evening) of the chalk hills and the rivers of this part of Herts for Dr Buckland[1] to use in his lecture this evening at the Society of British Architects, on the supply of water to London from Artesian Wells.'

In August 1850 Dickinson was busy making a model to illustrate his theory of percolation, and in February 1851 he lectured to the Royal Society on the supply of water in the Chalk Stratum. Harriet wrote that it 'was very well received, and he received so many compliments the dear old gentleman has been quite in spirits about it. He exhibited a curious model they have been making at the Mills and my husband helped as showman and all answered their wishes.'

By the autumn of 1851 another action against the Canal Company was in prospect. Their engineers had in 1848 sunk a well near the Cow Roast, an inn a little south of Tring, and were pumping water from it into the Canal. On 15 November Fanny wrote: 'Pa went up early this morning to attend a consultation with Peacocke, Cairns etc. for the Gd. Canal suit which comes on next Monday.' Two days later she continued: 'I am

---

[1] The Rev. William Buckland had just left the Chair of Geology at Oxford to become Dean of Westminster.

thankful to say that by the [Mill] Parcel we had letters from Pa and my dearest to say that the Case was finished, after being most "ably and satisfactorily argued by Mr. Peacocke", *for us*, and the four judges apparently quite favourably inclined, but as they reserve their judgement, it is still doubtful wh. way they may decide!' Dickinson was represented by Counsel who were to reach great eminence: Spencer Walpole was later Home Secretary, Richard Malins was later Vice-Chancellor, and their junior, Hugh Cairns, rose to be Lord High Chancellor. The scientific evidence established by Dickinson's experiments carried weight, and on 13 January 1852 Fanny could enter in her diary: 'The Judgement was given completely and entirely in dear Pa's favor on every point and was most thoro'ly satisfactory.'

John Dickinson wrote that day to his sister:

'This is not only a triumph, but a most important relief from anxiety, because the costs *on our side only* have run up to £1700 and upwards, and the [Canal] Company's are at least as much.

'This is the second lesson I have given to that rascally Company, and I should think it is the last time that *I* shall have to fight them.

'As I have succeeded, I feel now that it makes amends for my trouble and anxiety, because if the question had not arisen till after my death, I don't think my successors could have conducted such a contest to a successful issue, and most likely would not have dared to engage in it, in which case the Mills would have been irreparably injured . . .'

He continued his studies in the question of water supply and even lectured on it at the Royal Institution in February 1855. He was growing old, however, and Fanny did not think the discourse a success. 'Dear Pa began his lecture on the water supply to the Northern part of the Metropolis at 9 and with the help of Jack Evans's and Mr. Clegg's promptings got thro' it—but it was to my taste altogether a failure—the conclusions arrived at were unsatisfactory, he forgot half his matter, made mistakes in figures, names, etc., and was terribly nervous evidently, poor dear, and I was still worse—in short I felt some relief when all was over, but it quite upset me for the rest of the night.'

Dickinson's next controversy was with the City of London. On 23 October 1851 Fanny writes: 'Pa was down and full of a new Act of Parlt. inflicting City dues for coals upon this county and his Mills!' A coal tax, indeed, was levied on all coal imported into London and a district extending for twenty miles around the General Post Office, whether brought by land or water, and whether passed through London, or delivered twenty miles before reaching the City. It was an old tax, but had lately been increased both in amount and in area; it was widely felt that it now fell unfairly on manufacturers who depended on coal for their motive power.

John Dickinson continued in a state of indignation. He published a pamphlet on the subject in 1854, a second in 1858, coupled with a letter to *The Times* signed 'Turtle-sine-Dove', and a third in 1859. The tax was not lifted until 1889.[1] Besides these major campaigns, John Dickinson had some satisfactory skirmishes. On 26 October 1852 Fanny writes: 'Dear Pa came to dine with us quite unexpectedly after beating the Directors of the S.W. Railway at a public meeting so he was in capital spirits.' The war, however, ultimately went against him. On 16 January 1856 Fanny records: 'Papa's [South-Western] railway meeting took place and of course he was beaten completely, now he means to file a bill in Chancery!!'

Dickinson's dilettante son was at this time greatly interested in Indian reform. He had published *Letters on the Cotton and Roads of Western India* in 1851, and *India, its Government under Bureaucracy* in 1853, and in 1853 had founded the India Reform Society which preached the cause of leniency after the

[1] See *Hansard*, 22 May–3 July (Committee) and 1–8 July. The Royal assent was given on 9 July.

93

Mutiny. In 1858 Fanny writes: 'Found Pa very busy concocting a speech for the India House meeting to-morrow', but history does not record whether he spoke in favour of his son's views or no. Finally his activities found a more peaceful outlet in the affairs of Stationers' Hall. He was called to the Court in 1847; served as Under Warden in 1855; as Upper Warden in 1856, and as Master for 1857 and 1858. In that capacity he presided on 14 July 1857 over the great annual party at the Star and Garter at Richmond, and on 5 August gave the traditional banquet at Stationers' Hall.

In these years there was more drama in the family life of the Dickinsons than in their mills. For these it was a time of consolidation and quiet progress. Labour in the mills was for the first time regulated by the Act of 1850,[1] which laid down that no female or young person was to be employed before six in the morning or after six at night, or after 2 o'clock on Saturdays. A second Act of 1856 opened a new field of legislation by regulating the access to mill gearing and machinery, to prevent accidents.

The time had come when employers, and especially employers who had made a fortune, were fair targets for criticism. On 10 April 1850 Fanny writes in her diary: 'Heard from Mama ... there has been an incendiary fire at Ch[ambers] Bury which Providentially did little damage, but it is a bad beginning and a sad example in that country.' A second incendiary fire there on the last day of the year 'made Papa very unhappy, poor dear; he is so sensitive as to his popularity and the attachment of the poor around him!'

When Leonard Stephenson came to the Mills in 1840, he had found[2] the workmen in the millwright's shop at Nash 'nothing more or less than a lazy drunken lot'. None the less the Mills

---

[1] The Act of 1833 had applied only to textile-mills.
[2] I quote from the reminiscences of his great-nephew, Mr. Stephenson.

94

were gradually acquiring their own dynasties of faithful and trusted workers in every branch and at every level. Leonard Stephenson himself founded one such connexion. Of his four sons, Leonard became foreman of the Apsley paper department, Anthony held the same post at Croxley, and John and Tom followed their father in the Nash Mills engineers' shop. Between 1840 and 1928 the family was continuously associated with the engineering shops. The first William Peacock, who entered the Mill service in 1806 and died at the beginning of 1821, founded another dynasty. His daughter married Tyers, who succeeded his father-in-law as foreman of Nash Mills paper department, and he was succeeded by William Peacock, who in his turn was related to the Puddifoots, who worked chiefly as plumbers in the Mills. A third dynasty was that of the Rothneys. George Rothney was head clerk at 65 Old Bailey by 1832, and Daniel Rothney was manager of a department at Apsley by 1847. In the next generation G. A. James Rothney was for long at the London Office before he went out in 1870 to represent the firm in India. It had become a commonplace that more than one generation of a family should work together at the Mills.

At the same time the Mills were acquiring their customs. An engineer's apprentice, for example, had to be 'blown out of his time'. On the morning his apprenticeship ended he had to provide a nine-gallon cask of beer, which did not last beyond noon. A pound of gunpowder was bought at the public expense and a little cannon loaded, wads of paper being driven home with a copper drift and sledge-hammer. On the stroke of noon the cannon was duly fired by the apprentice 'next out', by means of a red-hot iron rod. The cannon, generally set up on the corner of the Mill Head, usually bowled over and over backwards for three or four yards. The ex-apprentice then went into the office to see the Manager to receive some fatherly advice, and, usually, a start as a journeyman at 28s. per week. When he came out, his juniors did their best to throw him into the mill-head, a custom on which authority frowned and in time caused to die out.

On one occasion, the cannon bowled over into the water, and a second one was duly made from a piece of steel shaft. Years later, when the water was down, several of the lads, on the look-out for fish, found the long-lost cannon in a very rusty condition and decided to 'do it up'. The top was stamped with the initials of all the apprentices 'blown out of their time', and these were added to on each occasion. This cannon was brought up to Apsley and was again fired on the usual occasion, much to the disgust and annoyance of the engineering manager, who finally had the cannon destroyed.

Half a century of progress had greatly increased the capital value of the Mills. In 1854 the Mills, offices and workmen's cottages were insured for nearly £140,000.[1] Their mechanical power continued to be increased. Most of the beaters were still worked by water-power, but a large steam-driven beam-engine of 40 horse-power, costing 3,000 guineas, had been put in at Apsley in 1845,[2] under John Evans's supervision. Another, designed by Leonard Stephenson, was set up alongside the water wheels at Apsley, to be used as an auxiliary when water was short. He designed it on locomotive lines[3] and christened it

[1] Batchworth Mills £26,100; Batchworth Cottages £600; Croxley Mills £12,200; Home Park Mills £11,000; Home Park Cottages £1,500; Nash Mills £16,450; Apsley Mills £29,910; Manchester £7,500; Old Bailey £16,000; Paddington £10,600; Belfast £3,500; (and a Nottingham branch). Part of the Manchester Mill was destroyed by fire in 1851.

[2] Ann Dickinson's diary tells us that it was first at work on 23 August in that year.

[3] His great-nephew tells me: 'It was of the horizontal type with central plain and expansion valves, two 12″ diameter cylinders by 24″ stroke. The main cast iron oblong open bed and frame was of the open box girder and bracket design. Mounted on a cross bracket was the belt driven governor of the open two round ball type. The speed of this and subsequent engines varied from 60 to 120 revolutions per minute, according to the work and arrangement of driving.'

'The Star in the Dark'. It began running on 28 July 1856, and was followed in the next two years by six engines of the same size and four smaller ones, all of the same type, each Mill having at least two, all made in the Engineering Department at Nash Mills. None the less water-power continued to be a problem. In March 1859 John Evans wrote to his fiancée: 'I never was so perplexed with business in my life. We are just now overwhelmed with orders and have no water wherewith to make them, so that I have to be constantly manœuvring to pacify people with the paper most pressingly wanted . . . I could not be away a couple of days without something going wrong. In a few weeks I shall have got more steam power at work, and then I hope things will go smoother.' By February 1860 a Stephenson's horizontal machine, built, like the others, at Nash Mills, was connected to No. 1 Paper Machine.

The London Office was extended by the acquisition of the lease of No. 64 Old Bailey, the corner house of Prujean Square, and most of the Square itself, in 1854. Two years later 66 Old Bailey and 1, 2, and 3 Ship Court (later called Boy Court) were added. No. 67 Old Bailey was leased in 1861, and 4 Boy Court in 1863.[1]

John Dickinson's last patent, taken out in 1855,[2] was a modification of his duplex paper, by which a web from a Fourdrinier machine was united to a web from a cylinder machine, giving a resilient paper for copper-plate or lithographic printing. The invention of photolithography in 1852 seemed to promise a great future for such paper; in fact the invention of more economical methods of reproduction soon made it out of date.

The general balance of manufacture was shifting from printing- to writing-paper as the postal reforms increased the volume

[1] No. 5 was taken over in 1918.
[2] 3 October 1855. Patent No. 2208. It is illustrated and described in *The Engineer* of 30 May 1856, p. 293. He had already registered slight alterations in the double-plate paper-machine on 23 September 1847, Patent No. 11,871.

of correspondence. In 1842, 196,500,000 letters were posted in the United Kingdom; in 1849, 329,000,000. On 17 July 1851 Dickinson wrote[1] to Charles Longman: 'We are doing nothing here but in Cards and Envelopes and not a line of an order have we had from L[ongmans] & Co. since your correspondence. The number of the Edinbro' is not on our paper.'

Competition was beginning to affect the manufacture of card as well as printing-paper.

'The card question (John Dickinson wrote)[2] must be gone into with a most rigid scrutiny for I am sorry to say a fearful reduction of price is necessary. A gross of small cards now sells for 45/– subject to 15 p.c. [discount]. I am fearful whether we must not come down to 36/– with 12½ [discount] which would leave only 9d. net. Take away waste and our sales are now ridiculously small. All our principal customers . . . say that they get supplied much lower and therefore "with much regret etc.", they leave us.

'Now I think with a very large trade we might bring the cutting down . . . then a fair and careful computation should be made of the value of the cuttings . . . It is quite the crisis of the trade for if we cannot make up our minds to a bold measure it must go. Then comes the great question whether we should not allow only 12½ on the envelopes. My opinion is that great allowances only allow scope for underselling.'

The Kentish mills were Dickinson's keenest rivals. On 27 April 1852 he wrote to Charles Longman:[3]

'I am really sorry to give an unsatisfactory verdict on the post, but it is only when you come to London that the actual test is arriv'd at.

'Joynson's paper is a different thing, and we are far from his secret whatever it may be. His paper 19 *lbs* the Ream is much thicker than our 20 *lbs.*, and it is no use talking of quality and surface with this cardinal objection staring you in the face, which

[1] J.D.E.
[2] Letter to Charles Longman, 15 April 1851. J.D.E.
[3] J.D.E.

actually stops a man from untying the ream. We could not do ourselves greater injury than by showing about this ream of paper and I fear that it has much hurt us in the envelope business.

'The paper from our Upper Mills is and always has been thinner than Croxley Mill paper, and I think there must be a something to give rise to the difference that we have not yet puzzled out.

'The Croxley is not so widely different as it was at first but in 2 Reams it is equal to 2 quires.

'I had for a long time imagined this to be solely a machine question, and that the Cylinder Machine paper was necessarily thinner, but I doubt it, for our 20 lbs. B. T. Demy is not thinner than others, rather in fact the reverse. Whether this defect in the Post arises from the nature of the materials or the mode of getting off the pulp or pressure in some part of the making process I cannot pretend to say, but it will not do.

'The quality is not quite so good as I expected to see it. There is some large and some small filth and in examining with a glass and in strong light I think I see marking of the milling plates, but I have no doubt that if we could make such paper and to handle thicker there would be a large sale for it at 9½d. .... Qy. Is that glazing with the paper Roll more suited for the purpose than our hard pressure between plates?'

The ever-increasing manufacture of envelopes was beginning to be systematized into two kinds: 'banker's envelopes' with the opening and flap on the long side, and 'pocket envelopes' opening on the shorter edge. Many experiments were being made in the most economical way of cutting them from the sheet. It was beginning, too, to be realized that a specially strong kind of paper resistant to wet was often needed for their manufacture, and John Evans made some successful experiments with new methods of glazing. In 1859 he patented[1] a method of burnishing by bringing paper into contact with one or more polished rolls, driven rapidly as compared with the surface speed of the paper being worked on.

[1] 23 March 1859, Patent No. 739.

One of the last family links with India had been severed when, in 1844, John's brother, General Thomas Dickinson, returned to England after forty-three years' service in the East. None the less the East India Company continued to be a valued customer,[1] chiefly for cartridge-paper for Army use.

The Minié rifle had been invented in France in 1849 and adopted by the British Army two years later. It was the first rifle so adopted to use a cartridge, and the manufacture of the cartridge-paper became a Dickinson monopoly. The paper was of the thickness of pasteboard, but rougher and more flexible, depending for its quality on the beating of the furnish. It is said that its manufacture imposed such friction on the cylinders that it was difficult to clear the small pieces by scrapers or doctors on the cylinder, and they had to be dived for at every revolution and picked off by hand between the felt roll and the cylinder.

The Crimean War brought a fresh demand for Minié paper. In September 1857 came the Indian Mutiny. Young John Dickinson and his India Committee were busier than they had ever been; a cousin of Fred's, George Barlow, died at Lucknow and his wife lost an eye in the siege; and old General Dickinson wasted everyone's time 'talking incessantly about Indy'.

A Government contract for 13,000 reams of the paper (always called Minnie in the Mills) was secured in the spring of 1858. 'John Company' was superseded by the new Council for India, but the contracts were renewed. None the less 1857 was an anxious and difficult year. In June the Dickinsons were much worried over the financial failure of the Whittingstalls of Langleybury, in which Charles Grover was heavily involved.

The new fashion for Christmas cards and Valentines, which had reached sizable proportions by 1850, encouraged the manufacture of fancy coloured paper at Croxley. In 1854 John

---

[1] A bound volume survives of their orders from 1830 to 1859.

Evans took out a patent[1] for making ornamental paper and paper bands by subjecting coloured or enamelled paper to pressure between metallic surfaces while in contact with lace or other ornamental fabric. Such lace-paper was in common use about 1860 for the more expensive Valentines and cards; and the ornamental bands were used to packet envelopes. The possibilities of such manufacture were increased by the invention of the first aniline dye—Perkins's mauve—in 1856.

John Dickinson, now seventy-six, was beginning to feel his age, and sprung his last surprise on his firm by deciding to retire. He spent the rest of his life quietly enough, more at 39 Upper Brook Street than at Abbot's Hill. He still entertained a good deal, though as his wife could not cope with any but the simplest housekeeping he used to get an outside caterer to provide his dinners. In February 1859 John Evans writes: 'On Wednesday I went up to dine in Brook Street with a literary party . . . There were twelve of us—Thackeray,[2] Mulready, Leech, Marochetti, Bell, Pye the Engraver, Van Voorst, Dr. Percy Laurence, John and I besides the uncle. The great guns were rather silent except Mulready who made himself amusing. I did not fall in love with Thackeray so much as I suppose I ought to have done, but I took a great liking for Leech, who has a wonderfully expressive eye with a most comic twinkle in it . . . I calculated the length of [Thackeray's] forehead nose and chin to be all equal and the upper lip two thirds of the height of either of them which gives a rather singular face.'

John Dickinson thought it would be interesting to become an astronomer, and built an observatory at Abbot's Hill in which he had a fine telescope set up. When it was ready he entered it

[1] 29 May 1854, Patent No. 1186. A careful distinction has to be made between the patents of John Evans of John Dickinson & Co. and another paper manufacturer of the same name working at Birmingham, whose first Patent (No. 7961) dates from 1839.

[2] On 21 December 1863 Thackeray again dined with John Dickinson; three days later he was found dead in bed.

by himself to observe the moon. He twisted the instrument about and aimed all over the sky, but could see nothing. Swearing loudly, he left the observatory and never entered it again. He had in fact omitted to take the cap off the telescope.

Old Dickinson amused himself by completing a novel, *Maidenthorpe, or Interesting Events about the year* 1825, begun some time before. To his family's dismay Longman's published it in 1861. It is now, and perhaps was always, unreadable. In June 1861 the Brook Street house was severely damaged by fire, and the old people and their household only escaped in their night-clothes. It did John no harm; he continued to attend fairly regularly at the Court of Stationers' Hall, occasionally looked in at the Old Bailey office, and occasionally went for a tour abroad. He still enjoyed writing to *The Times*. On New Year's Day 1869 he sent the Editor a letter, which was duly printed over the signature Delta, to plead that Britain should send an Army to assist the colonists in New Zealand in their war against the natives. Ten days later he was dead, just before his eighty-seventh birthday.[1]

John Dickinson had the reputation (in his son-in-law's phrase) of having 'a weakness for other people's wills though perhaps not for their feelings'. His own testament took, to say the least, a long term view. Fanny wrote: 'Everything is left to John [his son] and his sons after him . . . A codicil provides that of the £80,000 he leaves in the business £50,000 is to be paid to Trustees for John D. in the course of 10 years and during the following ten years 5 of the Barlow children and our 5 are to have £4000 in an order that he has arranged, one at a time . . . So Fred and J. have to pay out about £100,000 and though no money is actually left to them they get off paying a certain amount of Interest and have a very gradually diminishing use of the money for twenty years.' His partners were not likely to forget their father-in-law for a long time.

[1] He refused for some time to call in his doctor, on the ground that he was too ill to see anyone. His wife died on 28 December 1874.

VIII

TAXATION AND RAW MATERIALS
1854–1880

AS THE manufacture of paper increased to meet the needs of a larger and more literate population, the burden of the excise duty on paper grew heavier and heavier. By the middle of the century over 10,000 tons of paper was being made annually in the United Kingdom, on which duty at 1½d. a pound was levied. The use of envelopes increased the burden by creating new anomalies. In 1856, John Scott, of Charlotte Street, Blackfriars, an envelope-maker from paper not of his own manufacture, complained that he had to pay a duty of £14. 14s. od. a ton on his waste paper (worth only £19 a ton as such) whereas an envelope manufacturer (such as Dickinson) who could put his waste back into the potcher paid no duty on it. He challenged the Board of Inland Revenue, and in October 1857 such waste as his was also exempted. The exemption, however, was not extended to the waste on writing-papers.

By this time John Evans had succeeded in forming a trade organization, the Paper-Makers' Association, which had as one of its aims the abolition of the duty on paper. In 1860 the agitation on the subject came to a head. John Evans was all for the abolition of the duty; Frederick Pratt Barlow feared that it would be counterbalanced by a remission of the import duty on foreign paper. In fact Gladstone proposed to remit the duty on paper but to impose in its stead a duty on all rags imported into the country for paper-making.

In February 1860 the committee of the Paper-Makers' Association, with Evans in the Chair, considered what could be done.

103

On 18 February 1860 Fanny writes: 'Poor dearest off early to prepare for his deputations and public meeting. Young Fred met him at the meeting in Westminster and went up with the deputation to Gladstone and Milner Gibson . . . The interviews with Ministers were by no means satisfactory.' On 20 February she adds: 'Ld. Russell refused my dearest's deputation to-day.'

France, the country chiefly affected, threatened to retaliate by prohibiting the export of rags. In March John Evans 'saw Gladstone by appointment, who is determined to have his own way and is positive some new material will be discovered. Home late tired and disgusted.' Two days later Fanny Evans records: 'J. . . . went up to town by 11 o'c. train very much out of spirits and inclined to give up the whole fight, but at the House heard from Macguire [1] (who came rushing out without his hat to tell them) that the Emperor promised to recommend the Chamber to allow the export of Rags.'

Gladstone, in fact, was negotiating a commercial treaty on Free Trade lines with France, while the French Government was still undecided whether to remove the embargo on the import of rags into England. *The Times* of 5 March 1860 came out strongly against Gladstone's policy; it may be remembered that the Delanes and Dasents were family friends of the Dickinsons, Pratt Barlows, and Evanses. 'By the Commercial Treaty', the Thunderer declared, 'we shall be bound to admit paper, duty free, from all the world, although by these very States we are denied that without which paper cannot be made. We . . . have renounced all export duties, and by the Treaty bind ourselves neither to levy a duty on coal nor to prohibit its export. On the other hand, Mr. Cobden and Lord Cowley have forgotten to stipulate that France shall cease to prohibit the export of rags . . . We let France have our [raw materials]; and let her refuse us hers.'

[1] Presumably John Francis Maguire, at this time M.P. for Dungarvon.

The Times goes on to point out that rags cost half in Paris of what they do in London—30s. as against £3 for rags of the best quality—so that French paper-makers are in any case in a better position than the English. The English makers, as things are, might profitably consider migrating to France or Belgium. It reports that Gladstone proposes to reduce the duty on paper of foreign manufacture by as much as the Excise Duty at present levied on that of home manufacture, and denounces the scheme as unfair and unwise.

The whole question of rag and paper duties now passed into a political field in which it was argued on party lines with little regard to equity. In May John Evans went to France to interview Cobden on the subject with a view to the coming Budget. On the 10th he writes from Paris:[1] 'I have had on the whole a satisfactory day, having found Didot and Madame at home . . . I had nearly an hour with Cobden who was not so impracticable as I expected and seemed half inclined to admit my reasoning against classing natural and artificial advantages together. Mr. Mallet and Ogilvy were also there, but Cobden regarded the whole matter as one to be settled at home rather than here . . . I have also been to Notre Dame and the Sainte Chapelle and visited one of the largest Rag-merchants so I have done a good stroke of business to-day.'

The battle continued at Westminster. On 21 May Fanny writes: 'My poor dearest did not get home till 2.45 [a.m.]! He dined in the City and was in the Ho. of Lords during the great debate on the Paper Excise duty and the repeal bill was thrown out by an immense Majority of 89 Peers! Old Lord Lyndhurst who completed his 88th year this day made a most luminous speech on the Privileges of the Peers, Precedents etc. and Lord Derby gave one of his most eloquent and powerful speeches, perfectly smashing Gladstone and his policy, and his Budget and his Treaty!'

[1] J.D.E.

In June Frederick Pratt Barlow went down with a severe attack of smallpox, through which he was devotedly nursed by Fanny. John Evans and 'young Fred' carried on the battle. On 29 June Fanny Evans tells us: 'Between 40 and 50 papermakers (among them a foreigner who wanted to see Pam) collected for the deputation to Ld. Palmerston who received them standing and would not sit down for the half hour they stayed. J. had to open the speeches, which made him rather nervous. He said that the trade could stand this expense no longer, and begged that the Government would make up its mind what to do, and do it. Pam promised some sort of answer, but no answer was received.' A month later John Evans 'went with Wrigley to Ld. Palmerston without an appointment. He kept them waiting a long time, but when he did appear, was very civil, and entered into the question, and seemed to understand their argument. Then J. with Macdonnell[1] to Gladstone, who was very savage, and said they had no right to take up Government time in that way, but that anything they had to say must be sent to him in writing. So J. went back to the Old Bailey and wrote rather fiercely that he thought the paper-makers' affairs might have been worth a few minutes' discussion.'

On 27 July she continues: 'J. up again at 9 to collect forces for the deputation to Gladstone which was appointed for this afternoon. They were graciously received and the matter was discussed for an hour and a quarter, but G. was obstinate as a mule. However, it is some use to discover his tactics and line of argument. J. came home late and tired. Amused himself with coins at night.'

John Evans and young Fred attended the great debate in the House of Commons on the paper duties on the night of 6 August. The next morning Fanny tells us: 'At 12 came a telegraphic

[1] Probably James MacDonell the journalist, who was an expert on French politics.

despatch from dear Fred, Junr., announcing that our cause was lost in the House last night by a majority of 266 to 233!'

Gladstone's victory did not end the campaign. Free Trade in imported paper had been established, but the excise duty on home-made paper had not yet been repealed. On 22 March 1861 Fanny Barlow tells us: 'Poor dearest has to go up with a deputation to Ld. Palmerston and afterwards attend a dinner at Radley's to conclude the business.' On 18 April her husband 'went up to Gladstone, who was very civil and humbugging'. The next day he 'had to go up to old "Pam" this afternoon, and was not quite contented with his reception'.

The old duty on paper was, however, at last repealed on 14 June 1861 with effect from 30 September. No allowance for duty already paid was granted to paper-makers, though it was allowed to retail stationers, and elaborate and tiresome regulations for keeping paper warehoused in bond until the end of September were imposed. Dickinson's, like every other firm in the trade, suffered considerable inconvenience, and were also involved in many troubles over their Jacquard cards, on which 'drawback' was, under the official regulations, extremely difficult to claim. They got little satisfaction; but at least and at last the basic duty was removed.

Meanwhile the import duty on rags continued. On 9 October 1863 John Evans read a paper 'On the Manner in which the British Paper-Manufacture is affected by Foreign Legislation', at a meeting of the National Association for the Promotion of Social Science at Edinburgh. England, he said, imported about 20,000 tons of rags a year, which a less literate Europe was glad to dispose of.[1] France and Belgium, however, imposed an export duty of a trifle under £5 a ton, and the German Customs Union a similar duty of something over £9 a ton, on rags which

[1] In 1865 there were 390 paper-machines at work in the United Kingdom, producing 103,700 tons, and only 109 vats with an output of 3,310 tons. Dard Hunter, p. 526.

at that moment cost under £23 a ton for the best white rags. Up to 1860, when the Treaty of Commerce with France had been signed, a differential duty of 1d. per lb. of excise duty on imported paper had to some extent balanced the price of English and foreign papers. Now, however, the cost of foreign rags, due to export duties, was no longer balanced, and the foreign manufacturer worked at an advantage. In 1859 under a million lb. of foreign paper were imported; in 1862 twice that quantity; and in 1863 there were signs of its being once more doubled.

If the conditions of paper manufacture in England were compared with those of Belgium, they were clearly disastrously inferior; and a doctrinaire government was not interested. Only when the Conservatives were in, in 1860, was the import duty on rags removed.

It had long been recognized that the use of rag as the sole basic material for paper was a lasting hindrance to the development of the trade to its full potentiality. Ferchault de Réaumur had suggested wood as early as 1719;[1] Guettard swamp moss and various sorts of woods and leaves in 1741; and Schäffer other vegetable fibres and wasps' nests about 1770. None of these had proved practicable. In 1797, however, a pamphlet[2] issued in London suggesting the use of jute as a material for paper-making had been printed on paper so made. In 1800[3] Matthias Koop made the first useful paper from straw and from a mixture of wood and used paper waste. He took out patents for the manufacture of paper from straw, hay, thistles, refuse from hemp and flax, and from different kinds of wood and bark. He set up a mill to make paper from straw in Westminster, but it failed in 1802.

The end of the Napoleonic wars eased the international trade in rags, and for a generation nothing was heard of substitutes.

---

[1] On this and other early substitutes see Dard Hunter, pp. 313, 316, 317 and 370.
[2] *Ibid.*, p. 522.   [3] *Ibid.*, p. 332.

In 1839 Miles Berry took out the first patent[1] for the use of esparto, followed by another in 1853[2] in favour of Jules Dehau of Paris, and another in 1854[3] by James Murdoch. It was a tall grass growing in the Mediterranean area, particularly in Spain and Algeria, where it had long been used as a substitute for hemp. Berry proposed to crush it, steep it in limewater, and pulp it into a kind of half-stuff. In 1840 F. G. Keller, a German weaver, secured a patent for a machine for grinding wood to make pulp;[4] twelve years later his process was in commercial production in Silesia, and by 1867 in the United States. In 1866 Tilghmann took out a patent for the sulphite process of making pulp from soft wood. England, however, had no great forests of soft wood to exploit.[5]

In England the demand for rags grew steadily. Cotton waste came into demand for making wadding, cheap carpets, and other mass-produced goods, and the supply of rags steadily diminished. In 1856 only 8,124 tons of rags were imported into England, more than half of it from Germany, and a whole crop of patents were taken out for manufacturing paper from other materials. The cost of rags and, after a few years, the duty on them, made detailed costing of the first importance. Books of costs from Dickinson's Mills show the results of making paper from every kind of low-grade rags—dish-cloths, low fustians, Surats, Irish waste and Manchester baggings—with careful calculations, mostly in Evans's hand, of the weight lost in devilling, the chemical treatment given, and the resultant weight of paper and its quality. The cost and efficiency of various sorts of coal and of various sizing- and drying-machines were no less carefully calculated.

[1] 19 November 1839, Patent No. 8273.   [2] No. 1452.
[3] 7 February 1854, Patent No. 294.   [4] Dard Hunter, p. 376.
[5] Between 1860 and 1873, however, Heinrich Voelter took out several English patents for the manufacture of wood pulp. Shears, p. 27.

Meanwhile the use of other materials as substitutes or supplements for rag was gradually coming in. On 7 July 1852 John Dickinson wrote to Charles Longman:[1]

'Joynson has been making some paper with a large mixture of Straw and says it will answer well. It appears that it takes the size well, and handles extremely well, and thick.

'When it was tried at Bermondsey the knots were all cut out by hand. Might it be that these people cut it into Chaff, then make a sort of half-stuff or long pulp and sift out the knots?

'I have not been able to get a sight of Joynson's paper but from the description it is quite clear that it is not ill adapted for insides of all kinds of boards from Card Boards downwards . . . Rothney . . . says it was remarkably full in the hand and rattled uncommonly.'

In April 1854 John Evans took out a patent[2] for manufacturing paper by treating the waste refuse of 'the so-called Brazillian grass' used for plait and hats, by removing ligneous parts, boiling the remainder with limewater for a given time, washing in a rag engine and breaking-in in the same. It was to be used for brown paper by pulping; for better paper by mixing with rags; for white paper by boiling with soda, bleaching by chlorine or chloride of lime, and converting in rag engine, mixed with from 25 to 50 per cent of rag.

The supply of Brazilian grass from the hat factories of St. Albans and Luton was clearly small and uncertain, and the future lay not with it but with esparto, of which a supply could be assured. It was first imported into England in quantity by Noble in 1851. In July 1856 Thomas Routledge took out a patent[3] for the treatment of esparto and other raw fibres by a ley containing more lime than was necessary to render the alkali caustic, and afterwards by boiling and rinsing in a solution of carbonate or bicarbonate of soda. By the end of the year paper was being made from esparto at Eynsham, and the vegetable

[1] J.D.E.   [2] 28 April 1854, Patent No. 964.
[3] 31 July 1856, Patent No. 1816.

kingdom was being searched for other substitutes[1] without much result. In 1860 and 1861 the shortage of rags was so acute that *The Times* offered £1,000 to anyone who could produce a substitute, but no one came forward.[2] In his paper on rags read at Edinburgh in 1863[3] John Evans cites straw and esparto as the only alternatives. Straw, he said, was limited in supply and better used in agriculture; esparto was a product of the wild and not available in quantity. If it were cultivated it would become too dear. Yet he saw in it the only practicable substitute for rags.

Already, indeed, Dickinson's were experimenting with esparto pulp. The amount of soda employed, and the impure effluent obtained, made the manufacture of esparto half-stuff impossible in the Gade-side Mills, that were legally bound not to contaminate the Gade and the Colne more than they did already. In 1860—a year in which some 1,000 tons of esparto were imported into England—Dickinson's therefore joined with the pioneer Thomas Routledge in establishing the Ford Works at Ford, near South Hylton in Sunderland, under his practical management, where for many years esparto paper was produced and esparto half-stuff prepared for making into paper at the Dickinson Mills, all of which were at this time engaged in the actual manufacture of paper. The first balance sheet of the subsidiary firm, issued on 16 October 1865 shows that the first year was spent in experiment. In nine months 50 tons of paper was produced, of which the bulk was too coarse for anything but newsprint. In the second year it was hoped to produce 120 tons of half-stuff in every six-day week. The half-stuff from the Ford Works came to the Dickinson Mills in hydraulically-pressed round, upright canvas bales of about 3 cwt., and required to be broken small for bleaching and further working. It is related that the young lads used to sit by the side of the beating engines

[1] See syllabus of a lecture by the Rev. Professor Henslow, 3 February 1857, on the subject.
[2] Shears, p. 216.   [3] See p. 107.

to pick out any small specks and lay them on boards to qualify for a small bonus on their weekly wage of 4s. 6d.

Experiments continued. On 17 July 1872 Charles Longman wrote[1] to John Evans, who was abroad: '. . . We are going on quietly here but certainly with a diminution of orders. Routledge has sent us 5 Tons of Paper stock; Peacock has made some small experiments with it and finds it bleach very readily, but has not yet made it into paper. T. R[outledge] took luncheon with us yesterday. He is busy with his boiling patent but makes no progress in getting it to work; he assured me that it is not for want of confidence in the scheme . . . Esparto is falling but Routledge says that all sound grass comes from Algeria through Spain and that the practice now is so universal that all Algerian grass is sent to Spain and reshipp'd. He says no one can tell the difference till it is made into paper.'

In that year 115,157 tons of esparto were imported into England. By 1877 the demand for esparto half-stuff at Ford had so much increased that Fourdrinier's old Mills at Frogmore were taken on a seven-year lease, and Two Waters Mill was leased to prepare esparto half-stuff and make it into paper.

Even so, other substitutes for rags were still sought for. In 1880 young Fred Barlow went out to India and Burma to investigate the possibilities of bamboo shoots, which Thomas Routledge had suggested as a material for paper; but when he returned in April 1881 the report he had to write was unfavourable.

[1] J.D.E.

IX

PARTNERSHIP
1857–1885

JOHN DICKINSON's retirement left Frederick Pratt Barlow and John Evans as the active partners in the business, one in London and one in Hertfordshire. They were very different; fortunately each appreciated the other, though Fanny Barlow could never forgive John Evans for being a man of learning and not of fashion. Frederick Pratt Barlow was a good shot, a good cricketer, and in his own quiet way, good company; a man as clearly destined for election to the Garrick and the M.C.C. as John Evans was to the Athenæum. The Barlows' friends were no less in character; Corney Grain was as naturally among them as T. H. Huxley among the Evanses.

Frederick Pratt Barlow had four sons. The eldest, Jack, was destined for the business and was apprenticed to his grandfather at Stationers' Hall on his fourteenth birthday. It was soon evident that he lacked stability of character, and he found a more congenial career in the Army. The second boy, Fred, born in 1843 and educated at Harrow, had inherited his father's steadiness and quiet good humour, with a gaiety and sweetness all his own. Everyone who knew him loved him. He was intelligent, though not intellectual; and in spite of delicate health distinguished himself as an athlete, an alpinist and a fencer. In 1860 he began to attend Mr. Redwood's lectures at the Pharmaceutical Society on chemistry, and in October, when he was seventeen, joined the Mills, living in the Red House with his own furniture and servant. At the end of 1861 he was working at Croxley, but returned to London in March 1862 for another session of chemistry lectures before going on to Batchworth. In August he went to Switzerland for some months to learn French and German. On his return he began to work again in the Mills, though he never had to be so bound to them as his uncle had been, and was able to go to a great many balls in the course of the London Season. In 1865 he finished his apprenticeship to his grandfather and on 4 April 'took up his livery' at Stationers' Hall. In 1872 he was admitted partner in the firm. In 1877 he went off on a long journey to see the world and the possibilities of export trade: New York, Toronto, Quebec, Boston, Baltimore, Chicago, Denver, Salt Lake City, the Yosemite Valley, and San Francisco; on to Yokohama, Shanghai and Hong Kong, and back by Calcutta, Agra, Bombay, Madras and Ceylon—a journey round the world that lasted from August 1877 to May 1878.

His younger brother, Frank, was perhaps less brilliant but equally dependable. He too was at Harrow; it was a great disappointment when he just failed to get into the Eleven. In 1866 he in his turn went to Switzerland to learn languages, and two years later was working in the Mills, first at Croxley and then at Nash, where he lived for a time with the Evanses. His mother took him down there and records in her diary: 'Pa very grumpy. He hates Frank's being there and won't be civil to him and scarcely to me!... I trust [Frank] may make his way, do his duty, and win respect and esteem from the other partners as well as from the men below him. God bless and keep him in all his ways!' His enthusiasm for cricket was quickly reflected in the institution of an annual match at Nash Mills between the London and country employees. In 1875 he married Aggie Boyle, daughter of Admiral Boyle, and in 1877 became a partner in the firm.[1]

John Evans had been forced into the firm by family necessity,

[1] The Pratt Barlows' fourth son, Archie, never had anything to do with the firm, but entered a solicitor's office.

and had always longed for an academic career. He worked hard and steadily at business, but none the less managed to make a second career in learning. His numismatic interests already alluded to[1] secured his election to the Society of Antiquaries in 1852. He continued to work at coins. He wrote to Fanny Phelps in May 1859:[2] 'I have made some alterations in the machinery at Apsley which have wonderfully improved the paper . . . I have not been able to do much at my "great work" lately, my evenings have been so much taken up one way or another, and I have been wanting to get half a day at the Museum for some weeks and have not been able to do so. It is only an Account of the coinage of the Ancient Britons, but I want to have every known type of inscribed coins engraved, and if ever I can find time to do it I think it will be a creditable performance, though I say it that shouldn't.' The book—*On the Coins of the Ancient Britons*—had all to be written after a long day's work and did not appear until 1863. It was accorded the Numismatic Prize of the French Academy.

John Evans had done most of the scientific work for his uncle's researches into water supply in the chalk, and had thus gradually become interested in geology. He had to travel round the country on the firm's business, on railroads so new that the cuttings were still bare of grass, and so increased his knowledge of stratigraphy. He was elected a Fellow of the Geological Society in 1857.

It was in the field that lay between geology and history that his most important discoveries were made. In March 1859 he wrote:[3] 'In this bone cave in Devonshire now being excavated by the Geological Society they say they have found flint arrow-heads among the bones and the same is reported of a cave in Sicily. I can hardly believe it. It will make my Ancient Britons quite modern if man is carried back in England to the days when

[1] See p. 106. [2] J.D.E.
[3] Letter to Fanny Phelps. J.D.E.

Elephants, Rhinoceroses, Hippopotamuses and Tigers were also inhabitants of the country.' That Easter his friend Joseph Prestwich, a London wine-merchant who was also an able geologist, persuaded him to come out to Abbeville to investigate the claims of an old M. Boucher de Perthes, who said he had found man-made flint implements in untouched strata of gravel that also contained the fossil bones of extinct animals. They found his claims justified, and themselves saw an axe *in situ*. The discovery not only established the existence of man in palaeolithic times, but added a whole new province to prehistory: it may fairly be claimed as the most significant archaeological discovery of the nineteenth century.[1] Prestwich and Evans read papers on their discoveries to the Royal Society and the Society of Antiquaries, and Evans published his *Flint Impliments of the Drift* in 1861. In the following year he was elected F.R.S. Towards the end of the year he discovered the brains of the fossil Archaeopteryx, on the Solenhofen slate, and the jaw in January 1863. In 1866 he went with John Lubbock to Hallstatt in Austria to excavate, and made some interesting discoveries of the Early Iron Age. In 1872 he published a large volume, still frequently consulted, on *The Ancient Stone Implements, Weapons and Ornaments of Great Britain*, followed in 1881 by a companion volume *The Ancient Bronze Implements, Weapons and Ornaments of Great Britain and Ireland*. Both books owed much to his own great collections of prehistoric antiquities.[2] In his time Nash Mills was a famous address in the learned world. Not only the archaeologists came there—men such as Franks, Layard and Schliemann, but also the men of science such as Lister, Kelvin and Virchow.

Evans's archaeological work brought its own rewards and responsibilities. In 1870 he presided at Liverpool over the

[1] I have told the story at greater length in *Time and Chance*, p. 101 *et sqq.* and in 'Ninety Years Ago' in *Antiquity*, Vol. xxiii, Sept. 1949, p. 115–25.

[2] These are now in the Ashmolean Museum, Oxford.

Anthropological Section of the British Association, in 1878 over the Geological Section at Dublin, and in 1886 over the Anthropological Section at Birmingham. In 1874 he was elected President of the Geological Society; in 1876 Vice-President of both the Royal Society and the Society of Antiquaries; in 1877 President of the Anthropological Institute; in 1878 Treasurer of the Royal Society. In 1877 he received the honorary degree of D.C.L. at Oxford; in 1878 the LL.D. of Dublin. In 1880 he was awarded the Lyell Medal.

Neither his own researches nor his public work were allowed to interfere with Evans's business life. It is entirely characteristic that in May 1859, having discussed the authenticity and antiquity of palaeolithic flint implements at a meeting in London on the 6th, and left the next day for Ireland and got as far as Shrewsbury by train, having seen the current excavations at Wroxeter on the way, the rest of the week was spent in doing business in Dublin and Belfast, visiting Drogheda *en route*. On Sunday he went to look for antiquities at Antrim, Ballymena and Lough Neagh. He returned to work on Monday, finished his business at Belfast on Tuesday and got as far as Manchester that night. He did business there on Wednesday morning and got back to Nash Mills late that night.

His London antiquarian interests did not prevent Evans from playing a part in the world of paper-making and local government. He was the founder-President of the Paper-Makers' Association, and in 1872 served as the Chairman of the Paper-making Section at the Vienna International Exhibition. In 1870 he was Chairman of a Committee to establish a drainage system for Hemel Hempstead. In the following year he was nominated J.P., in 1876 Deputy Lieutenant, and in 1881 was pricked for Sheriff. In 1888 he was appointed Chairman of Quarter Sessions for the Liberty of St. Albans, of which he had long been Vice-Chairman. Yet most practical decisions in the Mills had still to be made by him, even if they were carried out by his younger partners. All his letters were written by his own hand, and at least up to 1876 he kept the cash-books of the firm himself. Even the busy executives of today may find cause to admire his energy.

John Evans's eldest son, Arthur, was a brilliant and rather erratic boy who flatly refused to enter the Mills. He went to Oxford and made a great name for himself in the archaeological world as the discoverer and interpreter of the civilization of Minoan Crete. The second son, Lewis, was of another stamp. Even in 1859 his father wrote of him: 'Loo is an eminently practical genius and so loving and tractable.' Like his brother he went to Harrow, where he got a prize for mathematics. In 1868, just before he was sixteen, his father took him to Stationers' Hall to be bound apprentice to Frederick Barlow. He entered the Mills in 1871. In 1873 he attended a course of chemistry lectures at University College. That autumn he went with young Fred to America, making an independent tour which included Niagara, where he swam the river a hundred yards below the Falls. On his return he worked for a time at the Old Bailey before coming back to the Mills. He became a partner in 1881. One of his interests was the Fire Brigade. A 12-man Strand-Mason Manual Fire Engine was bought in 1878, and kept at Apsley next the Time Office. In February 1883 there was a fairly serious fire at Croxley, and in consequence a full-size Merryweather manual engine was bought, and was kept at Nash Mills. It arrived just in time to deal with a fire in straw stocks at Two Waters, but not to quell it. The firm therefore decided that a manual engine was not adequate, and replaced it by a Merryweather Steamer, of considerable size. Its advent instigated the formation of a uniformed Volunteer Fire Brigade under Lewis Evans's captaincy.[1] The Brigade took part

[1] The original team were Lewis Evans, Captain; J. W. Stephenson, Superintendent; W. Pettit, Engineer; C. Chennells, A. North, H. Coker, G. Rickett and P. A. Thomas, Firemen;—Roberts, Coachman;—Palmer, Postillion; and S. Puddifoot, Driver of Hose Reel.

in the first of its many competitions in July 1884, at a Fire Brigade Demonstration at Berkhamsted Castle.

John Evans's third son, Norman, entered the Mills after he left Harrow, but found them uncongenial. When he was twenty-five he left England for the United States. He there attended some courses in chemistry, and later acted as chemical consultant to the firm, but never played any real part in its activities.

Both Frederick Pratt Barlow and John Evans thus not only worked for the firm themselves but also trained sons to follow them. The Dickinsons dropped out. John Dickinson the younger died suddenly in 1876, leaving two sons, but neither of them had anything to do with the firm. The Longmans, too, ceased to play any active part; Charles Longman died suddenly in 1873, while walking up from Nash Mills to Shendish, and his son, Arthur Longman, was a sportsman who had no wish to enter commercial life. Charles Longman's publisher brothers died in 1877 and 1879, and a fifth generation of the family took over the publishing business. Of them, Thomas Norton Longman married Frederick Pratt Barlow's daughter Florence, and Charles James Longman, John Evans's daughter Harriet, but neither had any share in the work of John Dickinson & Co.

J. W. Timberlake recalls those days in the eighties when 'Life seemed to breathe calmly, with similar work, walk and even talk in a revolving sameness for six days, and then a Sunday break. Village life was largely its own circle and circumference, and the outside world did not thrust and throb its collected tragedies, wars and rumours into every hour.' It was a country valley still, and the mills still existed among cornfields and hay meadows; men walked to work down lanes with hedges white with May in spring and fruitful with blackberries in autumn. The workers in the mills were still country people, owing allegiance to place rather than to class.

The organization and work of the Mills continued with little change. The increased use of steam-power made the coal supply more important.[1] The steam-coal for hand boiler-firing came chiefly from Staffordshire pits in narrow 32-ton boats worked in couples, with the horse relieved at half the journey. Three men of the Simpson firm and their relations the Septons for generations manned these boats. In the eighties this coal cost about 6s. a ton at the pit, haulage and stocking at the Mills adding a further 6s. 6d. per ton to the cost.

Paper went to the Paddington wharf by horse-drawn fly-boats, each holding about twenty-five tons, worked by the Sells family. They used to leave Apsley about 5 p.m., to call at each mill on the way, and to land their cargoes at Irongate Wharf about 7 a.m. to reach the Old Bailey about 9.

Working conditions in the Mills changed very gradually. In 1944 a man born in 1851 was still living in Bedmond[2] who could remember how in the early 1860's lads used to be taken on at 3s. a week, with a rise to 4s. after six months if they proved satisfactory. Later they were set to work to make 20,000 envelopes a day on the machine, at a daily wage of 7d. and 1d. a thousand for every extra thousand and another if none were broken. If, however, they produced less than 20,000 they received a penny less. Walter Lane, who was born in 1854 and started work at Home Park when he was nine, worked a ten-hour day as a sorter of waste paper for a weekly wage of 3s., rising to 3s. 10d. when he was fourteen. He was expected to go to Sunday School and there was trouble (sometimes a rope's end) on the Monday morning if he was unable to show his foreman the little printed text or other proof of attendance. He was earning 12s. a week by the time he was twenty. For a time, after a fellow worker had met with a serious accident, he had to be on

---

[1] In the seventies the water pumps, most of the beaters and the old No. 1 machine at Croxley were still driven by water-power, but if there were a shortage the machine could be coupled to the other three steam-driven machines.

[2] See S. G. Thicknesse, *Abbot's Langley*, 1946, p. 47.

duty thirty-six hours and off twelve hours, repeating this three times a week, with Sunday off; he was now earning an extra two shillings a day. Before his marriage at the age of twenty-seven, he was put to work at a paper-making machine, and his wages rose to 30s. a week. Every man in the Mills was given a Christmas box of 1s. or 1s. 6d., every woman and boy 6d., with time off to go into the village to spend it. If the Mills were not too busy at the seasons of haymaking and harvesting some of the hands would become agricultural labourers for a week or so. In Walter Lane's young days, Home Park had four machines (27-inch, 40-inch, 50-inch and 56-inch) making printing-paper, wrappers, cards, and 'Minnie', the cartridge-paper for the Minié rifle, which he remembered to have been so exceptionally strong in texture that a fifteen-year-old boy together with a half hundredweight weight had been lifted on a sheet of the material without tearing it. The work-people used odd bits of it for making tobacco pouches, as a variant of the pig's bladder then commonly used by mill hands. At Home Park it was the custom for beer to be served out to workers (at their own expense) twice daily; it was brought from the Bell Inn, the work-people leaving their work, refreshing themselves at the mill entrance and then returning to their jobs.

At Croxley in the seventies all paper-making men worked the 'journey' of twenty-four hours; out of these they were allowed two hours sleep (known as 'going to curl'), usually spent on a bed of paper shavings from the cutting-machines. They had all their meals in the Mill, with beer brought in from the Red House Inn. Day-workers worked a fifty-six hour week, starting at 6 a.m. and ending at 5.30 p.m.; women paper-sheeters worked from 8 a.m. to 5.30 p.m.[1]

The normal working day in the Apsley Mills during the seventies and eighties was (as it long continued to be) from 6 a.m. to 5.30 p.m., with intervals for breakfast, lunch and dinner. Everybody walked to work, many for a considerable

[1] Reminiscences of Mr. W. A. Stephenson.

121

distance. In the Envelope Department, each worker had a numbered saucepan and it was the cook's job to see that the workers' food was cooked to time and handed out in the proper saucepan. If, in dry weather, there was not enough water in the river to drive the water-wheel, the work-people would be sent home, perhaps to return later in the day, when the water had risen, and then to work through part of the night. The workmen, indeed, were expected to rise to any emergency. When news came through in 1870 that a ship bound for Australia had sunk, bearing a large cargo of paper from Nash Mills, the firm ordered the men and boys to work all day and every other night until the order was replaced.[1] Mr. W. A. Stephenson, who was apprenticed to his great-uncle Leonard Stephenson in 1882, remembers not only working on overtime until 8 at night about half the time, but also on six or seven occasions working all through the night on urgent work or breakdowns. The workmen took a personal interest in orders. Samuel Hosier remembered how at breakfast one morning the news went round that John Sands of Sydney had ordered 3,000,000 envelopes. Up went the tea-cans with a great cheer, for here was a full week's work in one order. A half holiday was usually taken, if not given, for Harpenden races, and for any local fair.

Old papers and paper shavings to be used again in the making of low-grade papers were boiled by steam in lead-lined vats about 7 feet by 5 feet by 4 feet deep. A young man stood on a plank placed across the top and pushed the paper into the boiling water, by means of a pole having a flat bottom 4 inches wide by about 2 feet long. The water was drained off after many hours and the stuff taken to the beaters. Boys, working on a twelve-hour shift, watched the pulp in every beater (at night by the light of a candle which occasionally fell into the stuff), and picked out any blacks or specks and put them on a small

[1] S. G. Thicknesse, *op. cit.*, p. 47.

board which was marked off in half-inch squares for easy counting. A full board brought a bonus of 2d. to their wages.

Boys as well as men wore oval caps or hats folded from a piece of paper about 2 feet by 1½ feet; Winter, the old millwright, wore a square paper hat.

Coal came by boat. At Nash Mills it had to be wheeled from the wharf on the canal, over the Mill Head Bridge and down the garden path on to the tip, a run of from eighty to one hundred feet. A gang of six men was made up to wheel in the sixty tons from two boats, the pay being 4d. per ton and thirty-six pints of beer (drawn from two barrels kept on the premises), this working out to about 4s. plus six pints per man. The other mills allowed beer for this work but were less generous in quantity.

'Pay Day' was not the same at all the mills, though all wages were sent out from the Head Office at Nash. At Croxley and Batchworth it was Thursday, at the Upper Mills it was Wednesday, but towards the end of the century the Upper Mills changed the day to Tuesday, because the workers complained that they were getting their money on an early-closing day.

The number of workers at first steadily increased. At the 1861 census 103 men, 264 boys and 125 women worked at Apsley, with 5 men and a boy employed as plumbers. At Nash worked 51 men, 21 women and 17 boys, together with 73 mechanics in the Engineering Shop—17 engineers with 5 apprentices, 5 blacksmiths with 5 strikers, 11 carpenters with 3 boys, 3 bricklayers, with 3 labourers and a boy, 2 wire weavers with 2 boys, 2 sawyers with 2 labourers, 1 tinsmith, and 11 labourers. At Home Park 47 men, 50 women and 40 boys were employed; at Croxley 35 men, 24 women, 4 girls and 95 boys; at Batchworth 29 men, 14 boys and 180 women; at Nottingham 11 men, 27 women, 7 boys and 18 girls. At Belfast 11 men, 14 boys, and 56 women; at Manchester 35 men, 48 women and 32 boys; at the Old Bailey 28 men; and at Leeds one man. The total was 418 men, 553 women and girls, and 495 boys, making 1,468 employees in all. When the next census was taken, in 1881, twenty years later, the number of employees (including those at Two Waters and Frogmore) had been reduced by mechanization to 1,434—581 men, 203 boys under 18, 532 women, and 118 girls under 18.

The regulation of factory labour had by now become a matter of Government concern. In 1862 a Royal Commission on Children's Employment was set up, which took evidence from eleven wholesale Stationers[1] but not from Dickinson's.[2] The evidence showed that in the firms they considered only 199 workers out of 3,284 were under 13, of whom rather more than a quarter were girls. Among envelope workers, however, women and girls predominated, and among 883 workers rather more than a quarter were young persons between thirteen and eighteen.

The resultant Factory Act, which came into force in 1864, chiefly concerned the employment of children, but also included some general provisions on sanitation and ventilation. It did not affect paper manufacture, but was valid for paper staining, and so concerned Home Park. In 1866, however, it was proposed to include paper-mills in the Factory Act, and John Evans and the Paper-Makers' Association protested that if the hours of all children, young persons and women were to be regulated it would lead to great inconvenience 'where one process of the manufacture is performed by boys and another subsequently by women. The hour of coming to work of the boys is almost necessarily the same as that of the men, but in many trades the women come to work later and may have to stay later to finish what the boys have begun. There ought to be a distinct provision that the hours of work of the boys and

[1] *Report*, p. viii.
[2] Fanny Evans records, however, that 'Mr. Lord came down on the Children's Employment Commission to see about those in the Mills'.

women employed in the same Factory need not be absolutely the same . . . Why should not the hours vary with the season of the year? . . . In the case of women who come to work at 8 or 9 a.m., who work by daylight only, and are paid according to "the piece", this enactment will appear not only needless but injurious.' Evans felt that the compulsory closing at 2 p.m. on Saturdays, so far as 'Young persons' were concerned, would imply its total closing, since the work of their elders could not continue; and pleaded, reasonably enough, that the Acts should cover all Trades and Manufactures, and not merely certain specified trades and mills of a specified size. In fact the Act passed in August 1867, while it specifically includes paper-mills, gives employers some margin in following the 'Accustomed hours of the Trade', provided that no boy works more than sixty hours a week nor more than fourteen hours a day.

In August 1870 the first Public Education Act was passed, giving each school-board power, if it wished, to require parents to send children of a certain age to school, provided that the age was not under five or over thirteen. In 1871 Bank Holidays were instituted, thanks to the advocacy of Evans's friend John Lubbock. In September 1880 an Employers' Liability Act made the employer liable in case of accident by defect or negligence, whether fatal or no, as if the injured employee had not been in his service, with three years' earnings as a basis of compensation.

The gradual development of the Mills' production continued. At the South Kensington Exhibition of 1872 Dickinson's displayed a paper-cutter, a set of milling rolls, a punching machine, a relief stamping press, and two envelope machines, one showing the old hand-feeding process and the other demonstrating the automatic feeder. Two women did hand-gumming, two black bordering, and two packed envelopes. A seventh made envelope boxes, assisted by a boy who hand-scored the blanks.[1] Frank Pratt Barlow was in charge, to the amusement of his fashionable friends.

Conditions of work in the Mills materially improved with better lighting. Up to the middle of the century the Mills were lit by hanging colza-oil lamps supplemented by tallow candles. The town of Hemel Hempstead had first been lit by gas in 1835, but the supply did not extend along the valley. In 1851 the firm set up private gas-works at Apsley, and in 1868 a pipe was laid that enabled Nash Mills to share in the supply, while Croxley and Home Park had their own gas-works, fired by cannel coal.

Apsley had become a village in consequence of the people whom the Mills attracted to it. The firm's responsibility towards it was expressed in 1871 by the erection of St. Mary's Church at the expense of Charles Longman, John Evans, Frederick Pratt Barlow and John Dickinson, Junior. They gave it all, even the bells.[2]

At Apsley Leonard Stephenson was appointed Manager in 1871; he held the post for seventeen years. Twenty-five years of envelope-making by machine had brought production to three million a week in 1876, approximately one-fourth of the whole production of Great Britain and Ireland at that time. Their manufacture was not yet fully mechanized at the beginning of the period. The evidence given before the Royal Commission on Children's Employment in 1862[3] describes the process of manufacture. Most envelopes were now sold gummed and folded.

[1] Reminiscences of Benjamin Tomlin, the boy, who retired from the firm in 1929 at the age of seventy. At this time John William Grover (1836–92) (son of the Vice-Provost of Eton and nephew of both Ann and John Dickinson) acted from time to time as advisory engineer to the firm.

[2] John Evans served as churchwarden 1871–86, Lewis Evans 1887–94 and 1899–1902.

[3] p. 10. The Report says that few children under twelve were employed.

'For gumming the seal of the envelopes a packet of them is placed, all with the lip open, under a small tap which communicates through a tube with a vessel containing gum. The tap allows the gum to trickle very slowly on to the lip, and the gummer's work consists in removing the envelopes one by one from the packet under the tap and laying them out to dry on open frames. This is done with great quickness and dexterity and one of the girls told me she could do 100,000 a week, working from 9 a.m. to 8 p.m., and leaving at 3 p.m. on Saturday; for that she would receive 10/6 . . . .'

An envelope-gumming machine was bought for Apsley in 1871, and that stage in the manufacture was gradually speeded up. The envelopes were all machine-folded, though the machines were fed by hand. The Report continues:

'In one place, where all the envelope makers are females, a girl standing at the back of the machine lays the flat envelope on a brass plate; it is then drawn away by a small roller towards the centre of the machine, and pushed into its place under the plunger by two metal fingers. The seal impression is then stamped on it, while, almost simultaneously, the plunger descending on it forces down a rectangular aperture, and the sides, as they thus become folded over, are lightly gummed. The envelope than passes underneath into a wooden tray, from which it is caught up by a second girl who sits at the side of the tray, the pressure of her fingers as she takes it being enough to make the sides adhere.

'Each one of these machines is calculated to fold 50,000 a day, and 45,000 is not at all an unusual number to be actually produced.[1] At one machine I timed the work, and found 36 produced in 30 seconds; the whole 20 machines in that place were said to turn out 3,000,000 envelopes a week . . .

'I observed that the girls who stand to feed the machine had nearly all acquired a singular habit of bending, or rather "bobbing" obliquely forward in regular time with the click of

[1] Mr. Samuel Hosier, who entered the Mills in 1875, remembered being paid a halfpenny a thousand for feeding blanks for folding. He could feed in 32,000 a day.

the machine as each envelope was put in. This action was quite unnecessary and apparently useless, for all could deal with the envelopes on the plate in front of them without stooping and some continued to remain upright as they did so. It had a peculiarly awkward and almost painful effect, as if they were butting at something, but I could not learn that their health or figure suffered from it. I was informed that the habit was for the two girls at each machine to change places from time to time, the feeder taking her turn at taking out . . .'

By 1878 the sham wafer on the flap, the last reminder of the functional seal, was given up.

A Dickinson price list for 1874 quotes for some twenty sizes of envelopes, in a number of wove and laid papers, all of them 'adhesive'. It also includes 'strong cream laid and drab wrappers for the Book Post', and has a special section for mourning envelopes, which were bordered by hand in batches of a hundred or more by women skilled in the work. A safety envelope introduced in 1868 bore in its flap two series of perforations, each series in the form of a curved line. Lifting or easing up the stuck-down flap inevitably broke the paper on one or both of the perforated lines, while opening by steaming spread the gum into the lower perforations, and spoilt the envelope.

It was decided to increase the space available for envelope manufacture at Apsley. Two old houses were pulled down and a fireproof building, 160 feet by 30 feet on three floors was built on the site by the firm's own workmen, in front of the Mill. It had dining-rooms in the basement. On 1 May 1877 Fanny Barlow tells us that she and a family party went down for the day. At Apsley 'We inspected the new Mill buildings, which are admirable, and the decorations of the immense rooms, which were extremely pretty and tasteful. Soon after 5 the guests and company being all arrived, they took their seats at the long tables in the immense rooms and the arrangements were so well managed there was not the least confusion and the eating and drinking commenced in earnest and continued for above an hour, to the great satisfaction of all, gentle and simple. Mr. Ward the new vicar said the Grace before and after, and at the end John Evans made a very good speech—the only one. Then the multitude proceeded upstairs, where they were seated as well as they could be and were entertained by the Japanese Conjurer D'Alvini, who is marvellous, and the Holdfast hand-ringers, whose music is delicious. We had some singing also, some very fair and some very good.'

In 1870 the Post Office had introduced postcards, giving De la Rue's the contract for a hundred million cards each stamped with a halfpenny stamp. The Trade regarded this as an indefensible monopoly, especially as they were sold with no charge for the card. John Evans did much to organize a protest and in the end the Post Office permitted the stamping of cards made by other manufacturers, if of the official size and thickness and brought to be stamped in lots of not less than 480. As a consequence the demand for thin card enormously increased. In 1883 (when nearly 160 million cards were sent through the post) a new card factory was built at Apsley, and in the following year a new department for dealing with its products. The card was still hand-pasted, with starch paste.

Nash Mills grew less rapidly than Apsley; it manufactured at this time the higher-class writing- and printing-papers, and specialized papers for reproducing maps and copperplate en-gravings. In 1870 it was making about thirteen tons a week; in 1879 about fourteen and a half.

In 1879—a year in which a storm in August completely flooded the Mill and stopped the boilers—Nash was almost entirely rebuilt. The old breast and overshot water-wheels were taken out and 'Hercules' water-turbines substituted. The Beater House was remodelled to bring all the beaters under one roof at one level. A new machine-house was built, and No. 3 machine remodelled. In the following year the first

Kollergang machine to be used in the country was put up at Nash Mills. Three years later the front of the Mill to the water was rebuilt.

At Home Park a fourth paper-machine was added in 1864. The invention of heliotype reproductions from photographs in 1870 increased the demand for coated paper, and this grew enormously with the invention of half-tone reproduction in 1877. Coated paper had been made by machine in Scotland as early as 1846, and, with this new outlet for it, its mechanical manufacture was started at Home Park in 1878.[1] At the same time colouring by machine was introduced, though hand-work continued to supplement it.

Work at Croxley continued with little change. In 1880 a large building was erected there for sorting waste, and in 1881 the beater-house and machine-house were rebuilt, a new paper-machine set up in place of one of the old narrow ones, turbines substituted for water-wheels, and a new steam-engine erected.

The Old Bailey office and the adjacent warehouse, built in 1861 in Belle Sauvage Yard, were Frederick Barlow's kingdom. His head clerks, Rothney and Patrick, came every summer to spend a week-end with the Barlows in the country, and in the winter invited the Barlows to an oyster luncheon in return. Fanny records that in 1868 she and her husband, her three girls, Fred and Frank ate twenty dozen, and went on to explore 'the warehouse and laboratory'. When Patrick died in 1879 Fanny wrote of him that he was 'one of the best and truest friends we ever had'.

The offices were partly rebuilt in 1863, and again in 1870. By 1877 the warehouse had been enlarged to hold a complete stock of the firm's manufactures, with a small factory for executing small and urgent orders.

The most significant development was the creation of a branch of the firm in India. About 1872 an agency was arranged with

[1] The machine was destroyed by fire in 1883 but was soon replaced.

the Calcutta merchants Messrs. C. W. Scott, who stocked three or four grades of printing-paper and two of writing-paper under their 'Star of India' label. George Alexander James Rothney, son of the George Rothney who was head clerk at 65 Old Bailey, was with the firm of Scott. He was a man of intelligence, a distinguished entomologist, and a good sportsman. He was a founder-member of the Calcutta Rugby Club, and served as Captain, Hon. Secretary, and Treasurer. In 1877 the Club fell into difficulties; its members were too transient to produce a regular team. Rothney got the Committee to accept his suggestion that the Club's assets should be realized and used to buy a trophy to be presented to the Rugby Football Union, to be played for at the annual match between England and Scotland. The Club's assets realized 270 silver rupees, and out of these the Calcutta Cup was made, in India and in Indian style, with three cobra handles and an elephant finial.

In 1880 the firm of C. W. Scott failed. Their Manager, Mr. Parker, was engaged to run a branch house for Dickinson's at 7 New China Bazaar Street, Calcutta, but was soon succeeded by Rothney. He instituted the 'Lion Brand'[1] as a recognizable trade mark in a country where many were illiterate, and Crimson, Primrose, Brown, Blue, Black and Green Lions indicated different grades of Croxley papers, and Deer Brands certain cheap papers for the native market. Rothney already had acquaintances in some of the Native States, where he had travelled on Scott's behalf, and was able to develop paper sales there and to secure contracts. At the same time Dickinson's Calcutta branch took up agencies for printing-machinery, type, and printing-ink, and so kept in touch with printers and publishers in India. About 1884 Messrs. Gordon, Woodroffe and Co.

---

[1] The brand represents a lion passant carrying a banner with the word RELIANCE. John Dickinson's arms were Or, a bend cotised between two lions passant gules, and the Pratt Barlow crest was out of an Eastern crown or, a demi-lion argent, supporting in the paws a cross crosslet. The idea that the brand exactly represents either of these is false.

were appointed the firm's agents in Bombay, and a staff of travelling salesmen gradually extended their circuits to cover most of the sub-continent, under Babu Kally Podo Ghose.

Such widely dispersed activities did not make much money in the years of trade depression of 1876–9 and 1883–6. In 1880 John Evans had to admit that the actual manufacture of paper was no longer profitable. The firm's profits were made not as paper-makers but as manufacturing stationers, and he regarded himself primarily as a paper-maker. His senior partner, Frederick Pratt Barlow, died suddenly in 1883, and he felt that the work of his generation was over. In 1885, when he was sixty-two, he gave up his partnership, though he continued to live at Nash House as the firm's tenant. For the next twenty years he was free to devote himself to numismatics and archaeology.

X

THE LIMITED COMPANY
1886–1892

O N 31 MARCH 1886 the firm of John Dickinson and Co. was formally incorporated as a limited company, with a capital of £500,000.[1] The capitalization at so high a figure incurred some severe criticism in the trade monthly *Paper Making*.[2] 'We very much question', their critic wrote, 'whether £25,000 per annum can be made, in these days of cutting prices, on printings and envelopes which are the mainstay of this firm . . . A large concern like this company will require a very large amount of management, which must be totally exempt from any small or one-sided views. There is a species of prejudicial feeling against this Company because it is believed that no servant can give satisfaction unless he be a Scotchman . . . Everybody naturally expects to see new ideas replace ancient ones in the change of an old firm, especially such a vast change as we have here in the case of Messrs. J. D. & Co.'

John Evans, who had initiated the plan of incorporation, retired; he continued to live at Nash House, as the tenant of the Firm, until June 1906. The Paper Trade presented him

---

[1] A new Companies Act had been passed in 1862. The Board Minutes of 25 May 1886 show that £60,000 Debentures were then issued to Vendors of the old concern or their nominees, followed on 25 June by a further issue of 1,000 Preference and 4,000 Ordinary shares, all of £100 each. Home Park Mills and 65 Old Bailey were left out of the Company's property and were rented by it at £750 and £1,750 a year respectively.

[2] 1 May 1886.

with a large silver tray on his retirement, as his wife wrote 'very handsome and very prettily given', and in 1892 the Stationers' Company voted him the exceptional honour of honorary presentation to their membership. In 1885 he had been re-elected Treasurer of the Royal Society, and newly elected President of the Society of Antiquaries, an office then usually held for a term of seven years. When his time of office was over, he continued to serve as Trustee of the British Museum. He was made K.C.B. in the Birthday Honours of 1892. After his retirement he devoted himself to the world of learning, and took no part in the affairs of the Company unless his advice were exceptionally asked on some point of past history.

The Chairman of the new Company was the senior partner, Fred Pratt Barlow. His long experience, his agreeable personality and his balanced character well fitted him for the task. The other directors included the former partners in the firm, Frank Pratt Barlow and Lewis Evans; James Harvey Brand, a London financier; and A. H. Longman, in virtue of his large interest in the business and his family connexion with the firm. George Alexander James Rothney, already a veteran in the service of the firm, was appointed Secretary.[1]

The passing of power to a group of younger men was naturally the occasion for sweeping changes. They did not wait, as John Evans and the elder Frederick Pratt Barlow had done, until circumstances impelled changes, but decided to act at once. A 'Reconstruction Planner', James W. Wyatt, with his assistant J. C. Hutchinson, was engaged for four years; one of the few men alive who remembers them[2] still recalls 'the hard Scots "r" of them and a wing collar'. Wyatt brought in four or five Scotsmen from his uncle's mills—Pirie's—where he had worked before; men who had been trained in a hard school.

The first change was to transfer all paper-making from

[1] Board Meeting, 12 October 1886.
[2] Mr. J. W. Timberlake.

Apsley to Croxley, leaving the older mill to concentrate upon envelope and stationery manufacture.[1] The firing of one set of four Galloway Steam Boilers at Apsley by Wilson's Patent Coal Gas generating plant had already been adopted in 1885. By 1888 the old steam-engine, the Stephenson engine 'The Star in the Dark',[2] the beaters' No. 1 machine, the gas-making plant and the water-wheel had been taken down, and the building was being reconstructed for the Envelope Department. The existing dining-rooms in the basement of the Envelope Building were turned into stock-rooms and new dining-rooms and a kitchen built on the site of the old bricklayers' shop. Further space was taken up by the processes of black-bordering, die-stamping, printing, gumming, cutting and box-making. A multi-colour printing-machine was installed in 1890. A galvanized-iron building was erected for a card and envelope paper store, and a giant envelope machine was bought.[3] By June 1887 Apsley workers were boxing three million envelopes a week, of which some 5 per cent were hand made.

The process of envelope manufacture had developed steadily. The blanks, punched out hundreds at a time by shaped cutters, were piled up on the machine's feeding-table. Two mechanical 'pickers', one shaped to fit the nose-flap and the other the tail-flap of the envelope, automatically coated with gum underneath by a rubber roller, were moved to lift a blank. As the pickers rose, a frame slid out under the blank, ready to take it immediately it became separated from the pickers by coming into contact with a stop-plate. This sliding frame placed the blank exactly over a rectangular folding-box, into which the gummed blank was then driven by a falling plunger. On its withdrawal four hinged pieces folded over the flaps. The envelope fell

[1] Board Meeting, 8 June 1886.
[2] Stephenson himself retired on pension at the age of seventy-five. He died in January 1905 at the age of ninety-four.
[3] Board Meeting, 26 November 1886.

through an opening upon an endless chain-rack, and while its tail-flap was pressed down and caused to stick, the nose-flap was held just clear of the envelope, which in this condition was then carried round by the chain until the gum was dry. By that time the envelope had come back almost to its starting-point, and was taken from the chain by two lever arms and placed with the finished envelopes in a long trough, each twenty-fifth envelope being automatically placed a little on one side, so that the girl in charge of the machine had only to put a paper band round each twenty-five envelopes as the machine delivered them to her; even this banding was performed automatically by some of the machines.

A price list of this time includes over a thousand kinds of envelopes differing in size, shape and material. There were seventy-two kinds of mourning envelopes alone. It is curious to notice that the list is so departmentalized that it merely states: 'Writing papers to match the above envelopes, cut and packeted, or in folio, kept in stock. For prices see separate List.' The list concludes with prices for sixteen qualities of white cards, four of waste cards, eight of coloured cards, and for four qualities of pasteboards in various weights and sizes, as well as book post wrappers, postal wrappers and memorial cards.

J. C. Hutchinson, Wyatt's right-hand man, was appointed Manager of Apsley Mills in 1888. He stayed there only two years; his interests lay rather in paper than in stationery, and he left to rejoin Wyatt at Pirie's. On 20 April 1890 he was succeeded by a young man of twenty-six, R. H. Ling, whose experience had lain chiefly on the selling side. He had a large staff to manage. In 1891 (when a census was taken) the envelope department employed 436 hands; 49 men, 39 boys under eighteen, 200 women and 148 girls: 37 people were employed in the stationery department, and 125 in the card. All told there were 695 employees in the Mill. Ling instituted self-registering time-recorders, separated the accounts of the envelope and stationery departments, arranged for an omnibus to run for the convenience of the staff who lived at Berkhamsted, and got the Board to fit up the meadow at the south-east end of the Mill as a recreation ground.[1]

The Engineering Department, long established at Nash Mills, was gradually transferred to Apsley in the years after 1888, and the book-keeping staff were concentrated at Croxley. Work at Nash, where Peacock succeeded Brond as manager in 1887, was concentrated on the manufacture of fine rag paper and on new Bouvier folding-machines. The Mill, however, was not prosperous. On 1 June 1887 'an experiment to test the electric driving of paper machines was sanctioned on the understanding that the expense would be moderate'. As a consequence one of the Nash machines was so driven, with success.

At the Board Meeting of 18 January 1887 the future of Dickinson plate-paper was discussed. 'After some discussion on the subject of the Plate Papers (in connection with Nash Mills) the Board considered that with the prospect of the failure of the Photogravure process to meet the public taste and a consequent revival in the Plate-paper trade it would be very desirable to do everything possible to preserve our reputation and "Speciality" in these papers and to take such steps as may be considered necessary (from the present state of the art) for the revision of our standard qualities and prices.' The manufacture therefore continued,[2] though, in fact, the future lay with coated papers. J. W. Timberlake recalls those days: 'The job I liked best was going round the mill watching the swirling stuff-chests, and the slow running of the high-grade plate papers; for Nash was then a very clean rag mill. Then the Salle, the sheeting room, for thick plate papers S and M qualities were sheeted most carefully for the least speck. Nash Mill plate papers were in high repute in

[1] In 1897 a Fire-engine Station and stables were built at Apsley and the engines and equipment were transferred there from Nash Mills.

[2] The question was considered afresh on 9 February 1892.

137

those days, for Virtue and Co.'s publications and Whymper's prints of the Alps and such-like exacting work . . . Special printing for book work was made, and a thin Bible paper for Bagsters, which was largely exported to America . . . Beater men and Machine men in those days always wore a paper cap, as a sort of trade insignia.'

The old beam engine at Nash and three Dickinson cyclinder machines were taken out, and one Fourdrinier machine put in. In 1890 two more cylinders were added to No. 1 machine and the manufacture of triplex boards was begun. In this year production reached thirty tons a week. The Mill continued to exist on a small scale: in 1891 it employed 56 hands, 38 of them men, and 54 men and boys on its repair staff.

Home Park was, in 1888, almost sentenced to amalgamation with Nash Mills, but was granted a reprieve. The manufacture of paper there ceased, and some fifty hands were put out of employment. Some compensation was paid to workers of long standing; work was available for experienced men at Croxley; but hardly any pensions were given. F. R. Pryor was appointed Manager, and a German chemist, Dr. Casimir Würster, was engaged[1] to work at Home Park, in collaboration with Lewis Evans, on the manufacture of chromo and enamelled papers. He was considered a great expert, whose secrets men would try to discover; the Board therefore decreed that no one in any way interested in the manufacture should be admitted to the Mills without the leave of a Director in writing. Würster remained at Home Park until 1894; in the last year he was instructed to teach a member of the firm the whole art of colouring.

In May 1890 a scheme of reconstruction for Home Park was authorized at a cost of some £4,000. Turbines were substituted for the old water-wheel, and a three-floor building was erected for a colouring-mill. There were now eight colouring-machines,

---

[1] Board Meeting, 28 February 1888. An Englishman, J. W. Leathers, had been engaged in 1886, but did not stay.

as well as a staff of hand colourers; cardboard was sent to be enamelled and coloured from Apsley and returned when finished. In 1891 the Mill employed 36 men, 16 boys under 18, 16 women and 3 girls.

The leases of Two Waters and Frogmore were given up and the half-stuff mills at Batchworth and Manchester were closed down.[1] The stationery branch at Belfast continued with a staff of 75 of whom 60 were women and girls.

The whole paper-making process (apart from the fine rag papers made at Nash Mills) was concentrated at Croxley. Sixteen acres of additional land (the Milestone Field) was bought[2] and an arrangement was made with Gonville and Caius College and the Commoners to accept another piece of ground in lieu of the grazing rights over a part of Common Moor.[3] Croxley Mills were considerably enlarged under the architectural guidance of John Evans's nephew, George Hubbard. In November 1886 it was agreed to build a new chimney two hundred feet high at a cost of £1,256; in the next month a new engine was agreed on for £3,160, and a new Mess and Dining-Room for £2,310. A new Salle, Beater House, Engine House, Clay and Bleach Mixing House, and Esparto Iron Sheds, were authorized in March 1887. By the end of that year nearly £25,000 had been spent. There were plants for gelatine, caustic soda making, soda reclamation, water filtering and softening, and two Artesian

[1] The leases were given up in June 1887. A bad fire at Ford Works in September 1887 ended the firm's corporate interest in that mill, though several Directors continued to have holdings in it. Routledge, the esparto expert, died soon afterwards. J. B. K. Grover, a family connexion who was manager of the Manchester Branch, was invited to work the Jacquard trade in that city on a small salary by way of pension; over fifty shapes and sizes of Jacquard loom cards were still stocked.

[2] Board Meeting, 14 December 1886.

[3] Ten acres of Furze Meadow were exchanged for just over seven acres of Common Moor.

wells. Two new Fourdrinier machines were erected in 1886, two more machines and American rag-dusters in 1889 and two esparto boilers in 1890. The Mill was now lit by 950 'incandescent' electric lamps, the current for which was provided by two Mather and Platt 'Manchester' dynamos each of 450 'lamp power' and one Siemens dynamo of '12,000 lights'. The number of employees increased; in 1891 an average of 319 men and 124 women were employed in the Mill and the office, as well as 91 men on repair work. There was an influx of new employees coming from all over England; their settlement, for the most part at Croxley Green, metamorphosed a country village into an industrial community. The firm built fifty new cottages, later called Dickinson Square, to accommodate a few of their families[1] and a house for the Manager costing nearly £2,000.

On the last day of 1889 Fred Pratt Barlow wrote to R. H. Ling: 'I am truly glad that you are able to speak so well of Croxley and its products. There lies the whole secret of our success or failure, and it really seems as if they had cast the die for success.'

The movement for a Saturday early closing reached Croxley at the end of 1889. The question was talked over in a conciliatory spirit and it was agreed that the Mill should close early or late according to the state of the Order Book. Six months later[2] it was agreed that Croxley and Nash Mills should close at noon on Saturday and that the men employed should have a week's holiday with pay. In 1890, for the first time, the firm gave £100 for the Annual Holiday Outing.

[1] The land was bought in March 1887. In March 1891 the Chairman offered prizes of £5, £2 and £1 for the best kept gardens in any Mill Cottage, and the Board gave an extra £10 of prize money. In 1899 the Board decided that anti-vaccinationists in the Mill Cottages should pay 3d. a week extra rent 'to pay for the probable expense of disinfecting and the cost of special sanitary precautions'.

[2] The matter was considered by the Committee of the Paper Makers' Association in February 1890.

The 'modern' mill at Croxley proved to be a less agreeable neighbour than the old one. The tall chimney belched out dense black smoke; the various plants emitted evil-smelling gases and 'bleach', and the dumps of effluent waiting to be bleached and fired added their share of smell. Neighbours complained; a new and more expensive method of bleaching had to be adopted, and compensation paid for fish killed by chlorine.[1]

Wyatt, the Reconstruction Planner, left the firm's service in September 1888 before the London Office had been dealt with, and John Evans was called in to advise Frank Pratt Barlow, who directed it, on its modernization. It had greatly increased in size, employing some 56 men and 12 boys, with 14 men and 3 boys at the Paddington wharf. The office was dark and airless, and the clerks worked sitting on stools at high desks. J. E. Hunt, the cashier, and his fellow workers wore black jackets, and, as Mr. Timberlake remembers, 'two or three inches of cuff. Cuffs were it—a rise it seemed meant more cuff. When not in the public eye *paper covered* was the rule.' Mill parcels arrived twice daily and a man fetched the bags from King's Langley Station.

A telephone was installed in 1886; it was taken so seriously that an employee had to ask the manager's leave to use it. Early in 1893 a private line was established between Croxley and the London office. In 1888 a private wire to the Paddington wharf was rented for £90 a year.[2] A boy messenger with a season ticket was put into uniform to take the bags to and fro between the office and the mills: 'you couldn't see him for parcels tied on'. At the same time it was arranged that a clerk from Croxley should come to the Old Bailey, and one from London go to Croxley in alternate weeks, to achieve a closer liaison. Such

[1] May 1890. The fishing rights were bought by the firm in March 1904.
[2] A telephone from Croxley Mill to Watford was installed in February 1890 at a rental of £30 a year for three years.

links were needed. J. W. Timberlake remembers of the Old Bailey of those days that few mill people entered its portals; 'if one did one talked about it. The word "Apartheid" was not then used—but it expressed the atmosphere between the LONDON HOUSE and the mills . . . But the genial and friendly two Principals Mr. Fred and Mr. Frank Pratt Barlow—kindly and welcome visitors—"Real gentlemen" the Mills called them —when they very occasionally came to the Mills, did *not* bring the London climate with them or their top hats. Now and then a traveller did so adorn himself, to add importance to some special inquiry, or emphasize some complaint.'

In 1888 a shorthand typist was engaged and a typewriter bought. In the following year a clerk was employed who could speak and write French and Italian, to deal with (and if possible increase) the business of the firm abroad. Office hours ended at 6, and the office closed at 6.15, but the house remained open until 7 when it was necessary to finish work.

The importance of salesmanship was beginning to be recognized. On 30 December 1889 Fred Pratt Barlow wrote to Ling: 'I have been thinking a good deal about our many repulses from the Stores, and it has occurred to me that a buyer in such a concern will not be bothered by looking through new samples of so complicated a character as ours, whereas if we got up one line expressly—in envelopes, cards and note-paper— exclusively reserved for each establishment, and of excessive value, it might be a bait which would be taken and enable us to get in the thin end of the wedge . . . Trade seems to be really on the mend and I am glad to see you taking your own line as to prices, and may you be successful in maintaining an improvment! We have followed others much too long, and I trust the time is fast approaching when we shall lead the trade in everything.'

In 1890, on the suggestion of R. H. Ling, a new catalogue was issued from the Old Bailey, a new show-room was fitted up and a counter-clerk engaged to display its wares.[1] At the same time, Frank Pratt Barlow, as Resident London Director, was for the first time given an entertainment allowance.

All the expenses of the new Company were incurred at a difficult moment. Political conditions were threatening at home and abroad; Ireland was seething with unrest, and France and Russia were uniting against England's colonial influence. It was a time of industrial and agricultural depression, with much competition and price-cutting in the manufacturing world. In February 1887 Edwin Wrigley wrote[2] to John Evans from Manchester:

'I do not know if it is possible for anyone, in any way, to ask the Paper makers how long they are going to continue the present *insane* competition. My experience in the trade is not by any means little—but I never remember anything like the "cutting" which is going on at the present time. The Wholesale Stationers are worse even than the makers. The abnormally low prices which have prevailed so long in the common news trade, seem to be extending to printings and writings.

'What justification is there for these great reductions in price? Is there any reduction in paper-making materials? No! There is a considerable advance in Bleach Powder, but this seems to be ignored. If makers can sell at present prices and realize a fair profit evidently we have some very clever men in our body.

'I find it impossible to keep pace with the reductions which are taking place. I make out reduced lists of selling prices for our travellers continually, but still I find that we are not low enough . . .

'Consumers are being unsettled by the continual fall in prices and will only buy from hand to mouth; and many complain and say that they would prefer to pay a fair price for paper, than buy at prices which I can't help thinking must be unremunerative

---

[1] The first paper table napkins brought from Japan were used at Dickinson's Annual Dinner in 1887, and imitations were soon being manufactured on a modest scale.

[2] J.D.E.

to the maker at least. I am not disposed to join in any combination or ring with a view to raising prices, but I think if the present ruinous competition was brought under the notice of makers that perhaps they might pause for a moment and think it worth while to try a little more firmness. The whole trade appears to be demoralized and utterly reckless . . .'

These conditions naturally found a reflection in the affairs of the Company. In the first year of their trading the profit on a turn-over of some £260,000 was only £2,051, or less than 1 per cent. Competition and price-cutting continued; it is significant that in 1891 the Board applied for 1,000 shares in the newly-formed Company of Messrs. George Newnes & Co., at a cost of £1,250, although they had no capital to spare; but they made the investment in the hope (which was realized) that it would secure them the contract for paper for the *Strand Magazine*.

The newly incorporated firm soon had some difficulty in raising the capital for their new buildings. In September 1888 they borrowed £10,000 from H. Cosmo Bonsor, M.P. (an old friend of the Pratt Barlows and a connexion of J. H. Brand's and of the Ormes of Longman's) at 4 per cent for a year, with a possible extension for six months; it was in fact only repaid at the beginning of 1892. In the spring of 1889 it was recognized that the whole state of things at Croxley was so unsatisfactory that Fred Barlow agreed to spend a week or two at the Mill to look into the proposed capital expenditure. At the same time Lewis Evans assumed responsibility for the Repairs Department.

In May Pratt Barlow submitted a report which revealed considerable mismanagement at Croxley. It was the shareholders' wish that a strong manager should be appointed. In June the Board decided against the introduction of outside help but agreed that they themselves should exercise more control. In July, however, Charles Hope Little, son of General Sir Archibald Little, K.C.B., became the Mill Manager, with James

Coutts of Aberdeen as Mill cashier. A German chemist, Dr Adolf Scheufelen of Darmstadt, was engaged for a year to test the products and processes of the mill.[1] In October Lewis Evans was able to report an improvement of £17,000 turn-over on an expenditure of £20,000.

In that month—October 1889—an important step in the development of the Mills was taken. It was decided to appoint two Managing Directors, one for Apsley, Nash Mills and Home Park (called the Upper Mills) and one for Croxley, with seats on the Board. These—C. H. Little and F. R. Pryor—were given salaries of £200 a year; Frank Pratt Barlow and Lewis Evans were given £300 as General Managers; and all the Directors were allocated a fee of £300 a year free of income tax. At the same time better attendance by the Directors was desiderated.

Croxley continued to be a source of anxiety. It was decided to close the Repairs Department at once, and to reduce stock. The building was reported to need a further £28,000 of expenditure, and this was met by the issue of that amount of Preference shares. In February 1890 Dr. Würster produced a detailed report on the Mill. He recommended the use of only the best grades of rags, and greater care in sorting and dusting. He advocated insulation of boilers, new methods of breaking and bleaching, and new kinds of loadings as used abroad; the investigation of new materials for paper, and the use of the waste in a brown-paper machine. He recommended modifications in the lay-out of the Mill, to shorten passages and avoid dirt; he advised more supervision in the Salle; more systematization of repairs, stores and so on; and the institution of an omnibus to Watford.

The Board accepted his report, with the additional recommendation from Little and Evans that negotiations should be

[1] The firm then had recourse to outside advisers, Norman Evans and Dr. Quirin Wirtz, who had a laboratory in Great Ormond Street. Norman Evans died in 1892, but Dr. Wirtz continued to act as the firm's adviser for many years.

begun to secure a railway siding at Croxley from the L.N.W.R.[1] The Directors agreed[2] to hold special quarterly meetings at the Mills to discuss capital expenditure on the spot. On 9 June 1891 the question of electric bleaching came up. The Chairman wrote (and his letter was recorded in the Minutes): 'Some day we may have to adopt it, but in the future let others try our experiments for us and let us settle down to understand and make the most of what we have got.'

The era of sudden change and adventurous experiment was over; it was time. In November 1892 the Auditors reported that the financial position of the Company was 'really serious', though recoverable. The Company's reserves of cash had in their opinion been too freely used for capital expenditure for the exigencies of trade. They advised a more stringent financial programme and a cessation of capital expenditure for twelve months. They advised that money should be raised from the Bank[3] on publishers' Bills; in fact John Evans lent some £4,000 to tide the firm over a difficult time.[4]

These difficulties enhanced the importance of two almost untrodden roads forward: advertising and export. Both roads were but timidly entered upon. The beginning of the firm's advertising was absurdly modest. On 29 April 1890 the Board sanctioned Ling's request to advertise black-bordered stationery in certain newspapers as an experiment, provided that not more than £50 a month was expended. Ling had in fact invented a new kind of mourning stationery patented on behalf of the firm as 'Court Mourning'. Instead of a black border all round the page and the envelope it had a black triangle in the top

[1] Lewis Evans's diary (J.D.E.) shows that negotiations for this were being actively pursued in February and March 1892.

[2] 12 May 1891.

[3] Robarts Lubbock became the firm's bankers in November 1892; Sir John Lubbock (later Lord Avebury) was a close friend of John Evans.

[4] 20 December 1892.

left-hand corner. *Stationery and Bookselling*[1] wrote respectfully of its 'unique and graceful simplicity. . .' and considered the black triangle 'an adequate indication of its sombre relation to inevitable human dissolution. Although but recently introduced to the world of tears it is appreciated by those who desire quietude in grief to such an extent that we understand the supply is scarcely equal to the demand, although there are upwards of eighty hands continuously employed upon it.'

In September 1890 the advertising of 'Court Mourning' stationery in magazines up to £400 to the end of the year was authorized, with the proviso that the magazines must be those run by customers of the firm. In October an additional £10 a month was permitted for advertisements in the Herts County papers. In January 1891 £40 a month for six months was authorized for advertising 'Court Mourning', as well as £160 for printing 5,000 notices to be stuck in shop windows. In November the amount was reduced. Queen Victoria, the ultimate arbiter in matters of mourning, stuck to an all round black border to her stationery, and her subjects followed her example. In June 1893 the Board turned down an application for further advertisement of 'Court Mourning'; yet when another application was made in September they asked for statistics 'with the view of seeing whether advertising on a large scale might be adopted with advantage to the business generally'. Eventually, however, they decided against it.

The question of export trade was more seriously and more consistently pursued, though as yet on a very small scale. In 1888 it was arranged that the envelopes for export, that had previously been sent to the London office for checking and packing, should be packed at Apsley, and sent by boat in their cases (which after a few years were made at Apsley too) to the Paddington wharf, whence they were to be sent straight to the docks.

[1] 11 August 1890.

The Indian branch office was already at work; in 1888 the Board gave much consideration to the starting of a Mill in India, but ultimately decided to postpone the venture. G. A. J. Rothney had left India in 1886, and had been succeeded by A. J. Millwood, who stayed there until 1892; Millwood continued the traditions of his predecessor with little change.

In 1886 G. A. J. Rothney went to Australia to see the firm's customers and report on the prospects. He travelled in a steamship, but it was dependent in no small measure on its auxiliary sails, which were carried away in a gale before they reached Adelaide. The storm also broke the steering gear, and for a time it was doubtful if they would reach port. When at last they landed, Adelaide failed to impress Rothney. After a short stay in Melbourne, however, he began to realize the potential importance of that city. There were already manufacturing stationers in Melbourne, and he saw that there was a possibility of trade with them. While at Melbourne he was offered, and accepted, the post of Secretary to the new Company, but none the less found time to include Sydney and Brisbane in his return journey. He advised the firm to arrange for a local representative at Sydney, to obtain business for them as an indent agent. In 1888 Leonard Stephenson, who had been Manager of Apsley for seventeen years, left for Australia, taking a Bouvier envelope folding-machine out with him, and making another link between Dickinson's and Australia.

In 1887 the Chairman, Fred Pratt Barlow, visited South Africa in search of health. He reported to the Board on his return that it was 'essentially a poor Colony and one which has hardly yet emerged from a very severe crisis. It is also very ignorant, many of the Dutch farmers being unable to read. The consumption of paper therefore is not to be judged of by the number of white inhabitants.' He recommended trading through London agents rather than through local representatives.

The only other field of export seriously considered by the firm was the United States. Mr. Percy Thomas (son of an old friend of the Dickinsons) visited it for the firm in 1887, but presented a non-committal report. He was followed in 1891 by Charles Barton Smith, who was employed at the London office. As a result of his report to the Board[1] 'It was the universal opinion that if we do business in New York at all we should do so in our own Name and with our own man in our own office'. As a consequence an office was set up in New York under W. A. Nosworthy. These were, indeed, small beginnings; but in them lay the seeds of greater enterprises.

[1] 8 September 1891.

XI

THE END OF THE VICTORIAN ERA
1892–1901

FRED PRATT BARLOW had led an active and indeed an athletic life, but had always been a delicate man. In 1892 his health began to fail. At the meeting of 21 June 1892 he resigned as an active Director. The Board invited him to remain as Chairman, but he refused. His brother Frank was elected Chairman on 22 November, and Captain George Wemyss was elected to the Board. As the Board was sitting on 1 August 1893 a telegram was received announcing Fred Pratt Barlow's death. J. Harvey Brand retired from the Directorate,[1] and Cecil Henry Thomas replaced him.

The changes made the Board more conscious of the length of the firm's history. Early in 1893 they asked John Evans to write a short history of the firm for private circulation. He refused, but in 1896 Lewis Evans produced *The Firm of John Dickinson and Company Limited, with an Appendix on Ancient Paper Making*.[2]

Various changes were made in the capital issue of the Company. In December 1894 the Preference shares were converted into stock, the transferable unit of the Debentures fixed at £1, and a First Mortgage Debenture Stock carrying interest at $4\frac{1}{2}$ per cent created. In 1895 the subscribed capital consisted in 2,500 Ordinary shares of £100 each; £200,000 of 5 per cent

[1] 7 February 1893.
[2] It was privately printed by the Chiswick Press, Tooks Court, Chancery Lane.

150

Cumulative Preference, and £100,000 4½ per cent First Mortgage. In that year[1] the question of the quotation of the firm's shares on the London Stock Exchange was raised. This was first secured in March 1896, when the Preference Stock was quoted at £110 2s. od. In June 1900 £100,000 5 per cent Second Preference Stock was issued.

Frank Pratt Barlow was a man who had no pretensions to brilliance but plenty of practical common sense. He had none of John Dickinson's eccentricity or genius, but much kindness and stability of character. His interests lay far more in the City than in the Mills; he was familiar enough with them, but had little interest in the technical side of paper-making. This fell more and more to Lewis Evans who lived first at Belswains, then at Barnes Lodge, near to Nash Mills and Apsley, and later at Russells, near Croxley. He used to visit one or other of the Mills almost daily, at first on a tall silver-plated penny-farthing bicycle and then in a motor-car shaped like a wagonette, with a high tonneau.[2]

In 1890 Lewis Evans became interested in a new composing machine that had been brought to London by a Swedish inventor named Lagerman. A company was formed and the machine manufactured in the Engineering Shop at Nash Mills. Some of the machines were employed in the London printing works of Messrs. R. Clay and Son, and some exhibited at Edinburgh. Mergenthaler's invention of the linotype machine in 1889, and its development in the next few years, then superseded the Lagerman machine.

For every entry in the machine order books at Croxley the exact substance of the paper in demy had to be given: that is, every size and weight had to be calculated on the area of the sheet in inches as compared with demy, 22½ × 17½ inches.

[1] 25 June, 26 November and 24 March 1896.
[2] I well remember its getting stuck on the hump-backed bridge over the canal in Nash Mills Lane.

J. W. Timberlake, who was in charge of booking the orders into the machine books, had already worked out the substance in demy to two places of decimals of all substances from 7 lb. and all areas from 300 square inches to Quad Royal, 2,000 square inches. He was arranging to have his calculations printed and registered when Evans heard of it, and suggested the use of a slide rule. This Evans worked out in 1892; it was on sale at Dickinson's London office at 40s., together with a book of instructions, and is still in use.

Lewis Evans continued to act as Captain of the Fire Brigade. A new fire-engine was bought for Apsley in 1893. The Brigade entered for competitions every year with increasing success, winning a national trophy in the shape of the National Steamer Shield at Basingstoke in 1901. Finally, in 1912, the team won the National Shield for the best all-round work.

The year 1894 was a bad one in the paper trade; several mills of good repute had to close down. Dickinson's, however, were more fortunate, and in spite of a fall in their Indian trade, partly caused by the decline in the value of silver, were able to make a modest increase in production and sales. Reconstruction continued in the Mills, but was in the main concentrated at Apsley. A railway ticket cutting-machine was installed there towards the end of 1892, in the hope of securing work from the Indian Railways. In 1893 the firm secured a three-year contract for the blanks for L.N.W.R. tickets. In the spring of 1893 it was decided to increase the envelope printing plant, to build a rotary card cutting room, and to add a floor for hand-folding[1] and black-bordering to the Envelope Building. A small book-binding department was set up. The new Writings Department was developed, by transferring Boxed Stationery to the Envelope Department to encourage the sale of matching paper and envelopes. Three thousand gross of Stationery Cabinets were sold in 1894. The Card Department was extended and reorganized.

[1] This was still important; 31½ millions of hand-folded envelopes were sold in 1894.

The Mill pay-day was changed from Wednesday to Tuesday to meet the wishes of the work-people. More important, over-time was reduced, especially for the women and girls employed. The normal working hours were in 1894 reduced from sixty to fifty-six a week.

On 14 August F. R. Pryor resigned, on taking up another appointment. He left at the end of October and R. H. Ling was appointed General Manager of the Upper Mills. He took hold with a firm hand, with a policy that yet further increased the preponderant importance of Apsley among the three mills in his charge. The year 1894 had been a notably successful one at Apsley. Contracts for six million envelopes for the Great Eastern Railway and three million 'pence bags' and four million printed envelopes for the Salvation Army had made up for a decline in Government orders. As a consequence Ling was able to persuade the Board, after a little delay, to authorize further extensions and improvements at Apsley. In 1895 the old mill-tail was covered in and a new dock and landings under cover built, while in the following year the old boat-loading shed was turned into a Despatch Packing Room.[1]

The Engineering Department at Nash had not enough to do. Ling proposed in 1895 that they should make eight envelope machines, at a cost of some £5,500; the Board consented, though registering its objection to the principle of giving the order merely to provide employment. At the same time four new folding-machines were procured from America, and three relief stamping machines were bought. In the following year a further £1,000 was spent on new machinery to enable the Mill to compete with the cheap commercial envelopes issued by Millington's and others. To meet these demands an increasing amount of paper to be made up into envelopes was purchased

[1] In 1901 the part of the waterway that ran between the buildings was narrowed by concrete walls; the walls were extended in 1905 and a new concrete culvert built in 1911.

from outside mills, some of which had to be trained to produce the special kinds of paper required for envelope manufacture. The envelope and stationery buildings were further extended and new printing-machines bought at a cost of some £6,500 in 1897. The members of the Board were growing restive under the flow of improvements suggested by Ling and sponsored by Lewis Evans, and passed the cost 'under strong protest'. Seventeen thousand pounds had to be borrowed from Robarts Lubbock & Co. at the end of that year. The Directors similarly resisted Ling's attempts to widen the scope of the firm's advertising. In October 1896 he suggested that circulars and samples should be sent to all the clergy in the United Kingdom; they advised instead that a restricted sum should be spent in sending samples to retailers.

Ling came in for a certain amount of criticism from below, for to make a profit on the envelopes sufficient to justify his plans he cut wages rather low. In the *Hemel Hempstead Gazette* of 26 February 1897, a set of verses signed 'M.H.' appeared under the title 'A Living Wage'.[1]

'Last week we were told a secret,
    And up went bounding our hopes,
They meant to give us a penny
    For a thousand envelopes!

'The wage is now but three farthings,
    And that is fearfully low,
For to make a twenty thousand,
    A girl must be quick, you know.

'It is just fifteen pence daily,
    You multiply that by five
And a half; and then calculate
    On what for a week we live.

[1] The cutting has kindly been given me by Miss Caroline Hancock.

154

'The girls in the North at spinning
   Are better off by a lot,
They can earn more with less working,
   While we down South seem forgot.

'All the foremen, and overseers,
   The clerks, and men at the mill
Get, we dare say, stiffish wages
   Watching us, and sitting still.

'We are but lassies and women,
   We don't want to make a strike,
Or any kind of a rumpus,
   'Tis not for of us the like.

'So please, see, good kind employers,
   Just what you can do for us,
We are good hard-working lassies,
   And don't want to make a fuss.

'Try and give us the level penny,
   'Twill add up quick in the book,
And soon you will see our faces,
   Wearing a less careworn look.

'As we trot in the morning
   Over the cold moor along,
We shall feel a bit light-hearted,
   And sing, like the birds, a song.'

The Manager, indeed, was something of a martinet. If an employee met with an accident at work, and was away for more than a fortnight, he received no pay for the first two weeks, after which he was put on half-pay. If he returned before the fortnight was up, he was given a gratuity, not exceeding half-pay, at the Manager's discretion. Lewis Evans thought this was hard, and at the end of 1897 persuaded the Board to join a Service Insurance Scheme, estimated to cost the Company about £1,300

155

a year. The Employer's Liability Act came into force in July 1898, and the opportunity was taken to increase the safety devices on the machines. Even in 1903 the old scheme of *ex gratia* pensions had not been revived, though some old employees were given 6s. a week when they were retired on grounds of age. In 1900 it was agreed that employees earning over 12s. a week should have a fortnight's holiday a year, those over 8s. ten days, and those under 8s. a week. Leave of absence for sport or pleasure was to be decided by the Manager and only exceptionally granted. The Apsley Brass Band was allowed six half-days leave a year.[1] At the same time a black list was instituted for men who had been dismissed by the firm, to guard against their re-engagement at another of the Mills.

Meanwhile Apsley prospered. The Post Office first allowed private postcards with adhesive stamps in 1895;[2] the permission resulted in an enormously increased demand for thin card. Four years later more ornamental cards were permitted. On 21 February 1899 the Board accepted a suggestion that a series of picture postcards should be 'got up' for the London stock-room; it was a suggestion destined to bear fruit in the years to come. The bookbinding department was developed, and the first account books produced in 1896. In this year further extensions for a Pasting House and stables at Apsley had been authorized, together with the conversion of the Old Mill House into offices. The first continuous pasting-machine was running on 28 September 1897. In 1898 a new boiler-house was built, with a chimney shaft 120 feet high; two years later the old square chimney and old card drying loft were pulled down, a new five-floor Envelope building, with fifteen electrically-driven machines, was built and a new water and sewage system

[1] November 1898. The Band had been founded in a small way in 1894. It joined the London and Home Counties Band Association in 1932, and had many successes, winning the Championship in 1935.

[2] Official postcards, sold by the Post Office, had been authorized in 1872, but the contract for the card had not been given to Dickinson's.

put in. In the same year a new policy on labelling was adopted, 'artistic but not fanciful'. W. Russell Flint, now Sir William Russell Flint, R.A., President of the Royal Society of Painters in Water Colour, but then a student at Heatherley's, was engaged half-time to design bands and boxes. In 1899 a corrugated-iron building was set up for the case-making departments, and in 1900 the expenditure of nearly £3,000 for a new electric light and power plant was authorized. It was at work by the next year.

By 1900[1] Apsley was developed as a mill with modern machinery, divided into four main departments: Envelopes, Books, Stationery and Cards, each of which could be divided as it grew unwieldy. Each department was self-contained, and each Manager responsible within his sphere for the buying of materials, the production of goods and their marketing. The weak spot lay in the want of liaison between Apsley and the London office, intensified by a personal dislike existing between Ling and Rothney. In May 1899, for example, Rothney, as Secretary, called the Board's attention to the decline in the London export trade for the preceding four months and attributed it in part to the want of effective sampling of Apsley products. Ling pursued a policy by which the Upper Mills had direct access to their London customers, which ran counter to the old division of work between the Mills and the London office. Further difficulties arose over access to the export market. They were resolved in May 1903, by Rothney retiring from the post of Export Manager while retaining the Company Secretaryship.

Nash Mills was far less prosperous than Apsley. Early in 1894 the Board agreed to spend £3,500 on the Mill; by the end of the year it had been raised to £6,500. Two of the three

[1] In this year about 3,000 tons of hand-made paper were produced in the whole of England, as against 647,764 of machine-made. Shears, p. 17.

Dickinson cylinder machines were taken out, and one Fourdrinier machine substituted. The old beam-engine was scrapped, and a new steam-engine put in. The demand for the plate paper, in which the Mill specialized, none the less dropped as more and more coated paper was used for reproduction; in September 1896 the Board had to recognize that the situation was 'very serious and most unsatisfactory'. They decided that the quality of the paper should be further improved, using nothing but rag for face, middle and back, to meet the demand of the highest class of engraving. None the less in 1898 a marked shrinkage of profit on Nash Mills plate paper had to be reported.

In that year a scheme of reconstruction was adopted, a new boiler-house and chimney were built, and a new boiler put in. In 1900 a battery of Taylor beaters and stuff chests were installed at a cost of £1,300 and the machine-house was considerably enlarged. A new 'making' cylinder was fitted to No. 2 machine and for the production of relatively cheap writing-paper to be made up at Apsley nine drying-cylinders, presses, calenders and damping rolls were added.

Ling did not like Nash Mills: a small mill with a long tradition of independence. He liked it still less after 1900, when Peacock resigned and F. G. Hawdon was appointed Manager, holding the post with that of Manager of Home Park, for Hawdon was a man of quiet dignity who could not be dictated to. In 1902 Hawdon reverted to the managership of Home Park only and A. Butler took over Nash. A note from Apsley, dated 11 July 1902, refusing an increase in rates of pay and other benefits, continues:

'Mr. Ling wishes me to impress upon you all that the Management of this mill is going to be conducted on very different lines than in the past. Each man will be carefully watched and be paid according to merit. For instance there is plenty of chance for a machine man who may think he has reached his maximum wage to aspire still higher if he shows himself worthy of it.

'The principle is merit, and merit alone. Every encouragement will be shown to those who are persevering and these are the men who will be pushed on.

'What we want is good paper, plenty of it, and in return you will get your pockets well filled.'

A Lancashire boiler and mechanical stoker were put in, and production went up.

Home Park made on the whole less progress. It remained a cosy old-fashioned mill that shut down to let the workers help with the harvest. At eleven every morning the Manager and the foremen used to adjourn to the Mill Cottage for bread and cheese and beer. In 1896 a new colouring-machine was installed to coat art paper on both sides, followed by a second a year later. The paper produced did well enough for wood-blocks, but many modifications had to be made before it met the needs of half-tone reproduction. By this time, indeed, growing competition and a consequent fall in prices greatly reduced the profit on art papers. In 1900 the experiment was made of running the machines night and day, but the increase in production was offset by a great increase in waste, as the skilled staff had to be assisted by less experienced workmen.

Croxley Mill remained the only rival to Apsley in importance, but its development at this time was far more restricted. In 1894, a bad year, the mill produced 6,900 tons, though at a small profit. In that year a new dynamo house was built and a new triple expansion engine of 700 h.p. was put in, together with ten large new beaters and a calender that would take paper 103 inches wide. The mill already had six Fourdrinier paper-machines at work, with two more Fourdriniers and two Dickinson cylinder machines in the old machine-room. In 1898 a small department was set up for coating art paper for magazine use. In 1899 the private railway siding, linked to Watford Junction, was at last secured, and a small locomotive bought.

A development of a different kind was the conversion in

1895 of one of the Milestone Field Cottages into a concert and lecture hall, rather grandly named 'The Dickinson Institute'. The enthusiasm of C. Barton Smith persuaded the Directors to build a more ambitious structure the following year, with hall, stage, dressing-rooms, kitchen and canteen, for which £50 a year rent was to be paid. Two years later the Institute was not in a position to pay rent, and was given the use of the building rent free.

These developments were on a small scale, and represent a time of slack water in the mill's affairs, partly due to ill feeling between Charles Little and C. Barton Smith. Little resigned at the beginning of 1899, and Barton Smith was appointed in his place.

Various changes were made at the London office. An extra floor was added in 1898, and electric light, supplied by the City of London Electric Lighting Co. at 4¼d. a unit, was installed three years later. In 1900 it was agreed that the office should close at 1 o'clock on Saturdays during the summer months. In 1899 a wharf and warehouse at 28 Upper Thames Street were bought to replace the Paddington wharf, which was found inconveniently distant from the City.[1] An office at Manchester was started under Mr. Waddell in 1893, one at Bristol in 1894 and one at Birmingham in 1896. New office premises were bought at Belfast in 1897, to which a small factory was added in 1899–1900.

Two Directors of the firm, C. H. Thomas and Major George Wemyss, interested themselves in the export trade, but it was G. A. J. Rothney who did most to control it. When he retired[2] he addressed a letter to the Export Department in which he expressed his beliefs.

---

[1] It was supplemented later by 44 Sumner Street, of which the lease was taken in November 1911.

[2] 20 March 1916. The Board had it printed and issued to all members of the export staff at home and abroad.

'For continued and lasting success in Export you must above all things be absolutely honest, not merely in the common dictionary meaning that you must not steal, but rather in its sporting sense that you must always be straight! Do the fair thing, play the game, and never so much as flirt with such traits as being smart, cute, sharp, or slim! Keen and hard and pushing will pass, but draw the line there. Your word must be your bond—not merely when it is convenient, but under all conditions.

'In dealing with your Customers, don't introduce or read-in some condition which was not in the agreement, which you never foresaw and which has arisen since—that must be a matter of arrangement and discussion between you . . . Young salesmen occasionally make the mistake, in their eagerness to secure an order, to omit certain conditions, financial or otherwise, and then, when questioned by their Chief "Have you arranged terms, etc.?" they are afraid to tell the whole truth! It is much easier to have everything clean-cut and distinctly defined before than it is to muddle it right after. Never promise what you do not intend to perform . . .

'Tell the truth, always the truth, and nothing but the truth . . . Don't promise anything that knowingly you have no intention to carry out! Recollect in reply to such solicitations as "Everybody's doing it" that what "everybody is doing" may not be good enough for J. D. & Co., or what may pass in Mud Street won't do for Old Bailey—that is, on the 65 side . . .

'The very highest code of morals is necessary in trading in India and the East. If the natives get to know, as they will in time, that you are a man of your word—a pukka sahib—always to be trusted in your dealings, you will gain their confidence and respect, and they will lean on you and trust you and you can practically take them into stock and make them loyal J. D. & Co. men; but if you try the clever—the cute—the slim —dodge, they will waltz round you and laugh, for they will be on ground where they know every turn of the game! . . .

'Keep clear of Law, that is, taking a case into Court! Before any drastic measures are taken they must be sanctioned by the Board after the fullest disclosures of all details and circumstances . . . Never threaten, or you will find yourself slipping into a position from which it is difficult to withdraw without loss of self-respect and dignity . . . Recollect that Export demands a higher scale of accuracy and a much higher moral code than the Home trade. You can't think how differently "facts" will appear when viewed 6,000 or 12,000 miles away in a totally different light, climate and conditions! There is much hangs round environment . . . Don't be afraid to own up to an error. We all make errors! The man who does not make them would be a worthless jelly-fish . . . Next in importance to a good name is a settled, continuous policy . . . A weather-cock policy is fatal, and so is the Searchlight Electric switch-on and switch-off method . . . Don't start a thing and then get tired of it and drop it, but rather don't start until you know you have a good venture, and, then, like the brook, "go on for ever! . . ." Don't forget it takes two sides to cancel a Contract. One party can reject, claim, refuse delivery (from quality, delay, or other reasons), but you cannot off-hand cancel single-handed. If the other side refuses to cancel, recollect we have no rights—no legal rights—and it becomes a matter for discussion and friendly arrangement . . .

'I conclude my Sermon by Chiron's parting message to Jason, the first of Exporters, in a way:

'"Speak harshly to no soul whom you may meet,
    And stand by the word which you shall speak."'

An office and stock room was opened at Jersey Chambers, 334 George Street, Sydney, in 1893, as a base from which the firm's representative conducted indent trading through all Australia and New Zealand. In 1895 A. J. Millwood, the firm's representative in India, went to Singapore, China and Japan, to explore the market, and returned by way of Australia and Ceylon. In 1893 J. W. Timberlake was sent as the Company's representative to South Africa and opened an office in Cape Town in 1894. In 1895 he persuaded the Board to buy land and build a warehouse and offices in Johannesburg. These he took over, Mr. Darling being appointed to the Cape Town office. He quickly developed a market for Bank paper, but his work was severely hampered by the South African War. Baden

Powell's famous siege stamps, issued in Mafeking in 1899, were printed on Dickinson's Oceana Fine, the most suitable paper available in the beleaguered town.

The outbreak of war in 1899 was a prelude to the end of a great century. In October the reservists were called up from the Mills; they were given a week's wages, and a promise that their places would be kept open for them. In November the firm began to subscribe to war charities by voting one hundred guineas to the Mansion House Fund and fifty to the Herts County Fund, followed by two hundred guineas to the Indian Famine Fund.[1] Stock was sold and the Bank Loan of £15,000 paid off. The Board decided[2] that it should not lend itself to any proposal for arbitrarily raising the price of paper.

Ling used the argument of the shortage of labour to get six more machines for Apsley; but his demand for £25,000 for Nash Mills was refused because of the war. In the first days of 1900 Captain Wemyss was given leave of absence to serve as an Intelligence Officer in South Africa. Stationery packets were made up and shipped as gifts for the troops in the field.[3]

The true end to the century came on 29 January 1901 when Queen Victoria died. The Mills and offices were shut, but a day's wages paid, on 2 February, the day of her funeral.

The turn of the century saw the rise of Dickinson's in the financial world. In 1894 5 per cent had been paid on the Ordinary shares, free of income tax; in 1896 7 per cent was paid and the General Reserve was up to £50,000.

---

[1] In 1897 the Board had given £105 to the Indian Famine Fund and the employees £74 13s. 6d.

[2] 21 November 1899. On 12 June 1900, Mr. Johns attended and expressed his views as to the danger of exchanging confidences on prices with other firms, particularly Scotch firms. On 13 November 1900, the firm refused to enter a paper-makers' combine.

[3] On 20 March 1900 the Board voted against a second shipment.

XII

THE NEW CENTURY

1901–1914

THE NEW reign and the new century began on a note of discouragement. The guerrilla tactics of the Boer leaders caused the war to drag on with little glory, and it did not end until 31 May 1902.

Peace was the signal for the Board to turn its attention to export. Much was still being done through London export houses, which were called on weekly by representatives from the City office. In May 1903 a young clerk in the London office, C. R. Gill, was made Export Manager, with half a dozen clerks under him as young as himself. For many years the team worked to build up world trade for the firm, with a system of overseas branches, subsidiary companies and local agencies, an elaborate private code, and a remarkably integrated system of delivery.

At first the policy of the new department, if it reached Board level, was dictated by Rothney. Progress was very slow. In October 1903 Ling submitted a report to the Board stressing the relative smallness of the export trade, considering the size of the Mills; the export sales, he said, averaged but little more than £5,000 a month. He advocated a vigorous initiative. In December, since the situation had not improved, it was decided that export orders should have priority. In March considerable anxiety was expressed over the South African Branch; much capital had been sunk in it but as yet it had brought in but little return. It was realized that not much could be expected until the country had had time to settle down; the South African Branch turned the corner in 1909.

Lewis Evans visited the Cape early in 1908 and did much to encourage Timberlake in his plan for a warehouse and eventually a factory in Cape Town. When Evans returned early in 1913 it was to find the branch in a new building, 27 Wale Street, opened in 1910. Evans was ill most of the time he was in Africa, but managed to get to Johannesburg, Pretoria and Bulawayo. When he returned he pressed for the purchase of the Durban store of which the firm already rented half, but the Board refused.[1]

The Indian branch progressed steadily. C. H. Thomas, one of the Directors, went to the country to attend the Delhi Durbar in 1904, but his visit was a brief one. In 1906 the State Agency in Travancore was taken up; in 1907 the Bombay premises were improved, and in 1908 offices at Madras were acquired. In 1906 the New York branch was taken over by Messrs. Perkins Goodwin & Co., an American house; in 1908 and 1909 the establishment of a branch in Canada was first considered.[2] An office in Montreal was taken in 1910, but made a loss in every year. The Sydney branch was moved to Wynyard Buildings, and its stock and travelling staff considerably increased.

In England fresh provincial offices were opened and others closed. The Belfast office was nearly given up in August 1902; it was reprieved, but continued to make a small loss every year. A branch office at Leeds was opened in 1905 and the Birmingham office housed at 162 Edmund Street. The Bristol office was established in leasehold premises at West India House in 1906. New offices were opened at Nottingham and Liverpool in 1908; the latter was closed four years later. In 1911 a small factory,

---

[1] The store was later burnt, and the firm then purchased a plot of land and built a store.

[2] Board Meetings, 29 July 1908 and 19 June 1909.

Albert Mills, was bought at Manchester from the Standard Envelope Co. and used chiefly for local orders.

In 1903 a plan was brought forward to get all the London offices under one roof, but the Board refused to give up 65 Old Bailey.[1] Instead the London Stationery department was moved from the Old Bailey to 27 Upper Thames Street and put under the Upper Mills organization in January 1904. Eighteen months later the Paddington wharf was also made a part of this organization. The changes represented a victory for Ling, and considerably increased his powers and responsibilities.

At this time, indeed, the family directors were beginning to play a secondary part. Frank Pratt Barlow was growing old, and retired in July 1912; Lewis Evans succeeded him as Chairman. Evans was a man of charm and sensibility. He had inherited some of his father's eye for quality and his flair for historical interest; his collection of ancient scientific instruments became one of the finest in the world. It was accepted in 1925 by the University of Oxford, who gave him the degree of D.Sc. *honoris causa*. He took a considerable interest in politics; he 'nursed' the West Herts constituency for a time, and in 1903 was invited by Joseph Chamberlain to serve on a special committee on Tariff Reform as the representative of the papermaking interest. He was a keen Churchman, and worked at the Diocesan finances, and in 1902 served as President of the Hertfordshire Natural History Society.[2] Born and bred at Nash Mills, he had a lifelong familiarity with the processes of papermaking, and an innate sense of the qualities of paper. He had never seriously trained as an engineer, but his father and

---

[1] In 1907 John Evans transferred his interest in 65 Old Bailey and Home Park Mill to Lewis Evans.

[2] His presidential address, 'Progress in the Nineteenth Century', is printed in its *Transactions*, XI, pt. 4, June 1902, p.105. He was a Fellow of the Society of Antiquaries and of the Royal Astronomical Society.

Stephenson had given him a sound working knowledge of engineering in so far as it concerned paper-making. He had the same knowledge, such as no outsider could possess, of pulp and paper, boards and stationery; and he had known the old employees of the Mill all his life. Yet he lacked his father's power of decision, and his more massive intellectual qualities. He had refused to go to Oxford, and had not benefited by academic discipline. His passion for new inventions was not always harnessed to the practical; he often wished to try what was new, with little thought of actual cost or potential profit. Yet this attitude of mind made it easier than it might otherwise have been to avoid stagnation in the Mills, already highly organized; and the counsels of other men, wiser in finance, acted as a counterpoise to innovation. Reginald Bonsor, who had joined the Company in 1901, became a Director in 1905; Robert Pratt Barlow, Frank's younger son, joined the Board in 1912.

In 1907 £50,000 Second Preference shares[1] were issued; the issue was over subscribed. In 1912, when the net profits amounted to nearly £99,500, the issue of £400 4½ per cent First Mortgage Debentures was authorized, and £250,000 of them issued, £100,000 to holders of the existing debentures, in exchange, with a cash bonus of 5 per cent, and £150,000 to the public at par.

The years passed with the normal fluctuations of trade. Much competition was seen in 1901 from the northern mills, which were short of orders, and a consequent drop in prices; it proved, however, to be a profitable year. Profits dropped a little in 1908, but rose in 1909. The year 1910 was a very good one, and after it £250,000 was taken from Reserve and distributed as a bonus in shares to the Ordinary shareholders. No less prosperous was 1911, but a far more anxious year, for there was a coal strike in March and April, and coal had to be bought at famine

[1] Converted into Stock, 23 October 1907.

prices to keep the Mills going. The coal strike was followed by strikes of dockers, carmen and railwaymen, which dislocated dispatch. In August the strikes were reflected in unrest among some workers in the Envelope and Book-printing departments at Apsley, culminating in a few hours absence from work; fortunately the difficulty was quickly settled.

The organization of the Mills and offices progressed under Ling's inspiration. In July 1903 a scheme was instituted to avoid Sunday labour as far as possible. At Nash Mills, for example, the machines were to be shut down at nine or ten on Saturday night, and got ready for Monday morning, thus allowing the men to go home at midnight. Beatermen and their helpers, kneadermen, repair men and the double staff for the machines were to come in at five on Monday morning, the extra shift going home as soon as the machines had got going.

A circular of August 1903 encouraged travellers to make suggestions to the Mill Managers on the lines that were in demand. A letter from Ling to the Managers of the Upper Mills foreshadowed their general development, and stressed the importance of the quality of the men who were taken into the Mills, from office boys upwards, saying that it might pay in the long run to give beginners better wages. At the end of the year a new Financial Department was instituted in London, covering all the Mills, and financed by a $1\frac{1}{4}$ per cent charge on sales.

The year 1904 witnessed the Centenary of the firm.[1] All the workers (at home and abroad) were given double wages or salaries for the week beginning 29 March; twenty additional pensions were instituted (in addition to twenty already existing) for work-people leaving the Mills under circumstances of hardship or after many years' service; and donations of one hundred guineas were given to the West Herts Infirmary, the Watford

[1] A special supplement was printed to the *Hemel Hempstead Gazette* on 16 April.

District Hospital, the Herts Convalescent Home, and the Apsley and King's Langley Parish Rooms. Additional class-rooms and bathrooms were added to the Dickinson Institute at Croxley.

The years that led up to the general slump of 1908 were difficult, and were marked by no great developments. An instruction to the Managers, dated 17 July 1907, marks the difficulty: 'That no hint of either the number of our hands, or quantity of work manufactured in our Factory should be given to any outside people, whether in the trade or otherwise, nor to divulge in any way the class of machinery that we use in our factories, especially when we put down anything of a new and individual character.'

In 1907 the firm's old generous plan of Christmas presents, dating back to John Dickinson himself, was revised; in 1908 a stringent set of rules to promote economy were issued to the Mill Managers. In February 1909 a further letter, drafted it would seem by Ling, was issued to them.

'The divulgence of any information relating to the Company's business to persons outside the Company's service, either by word of mouth or by writing, is forbidden. Making notes for any other purpose than use in the Company's service of matters of any kind relating to the Company's business is not allowed. All notes, price lists, samples, and general information acquired and used in the conduct of the Company's business belong solely to the Company, must be kept on the Company's premises, and delivered up on leaving the Company's service.

'The penalty for a breach in observance of above is instant dismissal.'

The tension of the times was evidenced in an attempt at arson with petrol in the stock room behind Ling's office at Apsley. Little damage was done; a reward of £100 was offered for the discovery of the *pétroleur*, but was never claimed.

In May 1910 monthly meetings of the Mill Managers were

instituted; it was a far greater measure of devolution than was realized by the Board. The question of holidays was further codified: Managers were to have three weeks holiday with pay, foremen a fortnight, and boilermen (after twelve months' employment) a week.

In 1911 the Directors recommended to the Annual General Meeting, who accepted the resolution, 'That a sum of £10,000 be set aside out of profits to form the nucleus of a special Service Fund for the Apsley Departments to be automatically increased by a charge on the profits of those Departments, the object being to have some fund available from which deserving Representatives, who have from one cause or another to leave the Company's service, may be remunerated. Some such system may well be extended to other Departments and Branches as opportunity offers.' On 13 March 1912 the Board resolved,

'to start a list of the salaried staffs at the Old Bailey, Croxley and abroad who in recognition of long and meritorious service will be eligible for pensions when they retire.

'Inclusion in the list will be on the recommendation of a Cttee. composed of the Secretary, the Manager of the O.B. Paper Dept. and the Manager of Croxley Mills.

'Each pension will be considered on its merits by the Committee and the final decision will rest with the Board. When a member's name is placed on the List the fact will be notified to him. A name may be removed from the List on the recommendation of the Cttee. but the fact must be notified to the person concerned.'

By the end of 1911 the Company's existing voluntary contributory insurance scheme was closed for workers in the United Kingdom. In May 1912 the National Insurance Act came into force, all workers over sixteen years of age being compulsorily insured.[1] The firm's sense of responsibility for the workers was increased; in that year a Labour Bureau was established

[1] On 30 April 1913 a resolution was passed that no one was to be employed on the staff of the Old Bailey without a medical certificate.

at Apsley where all applicants for casual work were to be interviewed.

In 1901 there was a bad accident at Apsley; the flywheel of the milling-room engine, weighing more than eight tons, blew to pieces, wrecking the engine, the rooms over and the stairs alongside. Providentially no one was hurt, but the general question of safety was further considered. The Apsley buildings were protected by the laying of a fire-main and the setting up of fire-pumps, with sprinklers added in 1904, and the property insured for £150,000. In 1913 the factory hours were changed from 6-8, 8.30-12.30 and 1.30-5.30 to two spells, 8-12.30 and 1.30-6. Rates were adjusted so that no one got less wages. In 1912 a system of Mill Records was started, to record the history of each Mill; it has unfortunately since lapsed.

The importance of Apsley in the hierarchy of the mills continued to be emphasized. A further £8,000 odd expenditure upon Apsley was made in 1902, with nearly as much again in the following six months. Ling asked for an addition to the Envelope Department, but the Board refused it until the weekly output averaged more than thirty million. The Nash Mills engineering department was short of work, and he asked that they should be instructed to make three Royal envelope machines for Apsley. The Board refused, and as a consequence the Engineering Department was reduced to the level of a repair shop and moved to Apsley in 1903. In that year the first floor of the old envelope block was turned into the women's dining-room, the men took over their former dining-room, and the men's old dining-room was turned into smiths' and paint shops and engineering stores. In the following year[1] a scheme was passed authorizing the expenditure of some £10,000 on storage space for material, finished stock, export stock, a despatch and packing room and yard and a new dock and wharf. A new time office and a new stable for the

[1] 17 August 1904. The extensions were carried out in 1905.

boat horses were built, and a new travelling electric crane purchased.

The year 1905 saw further developments at Apsley. The adjacent 'Salmon' meadow, for years a Naboth's vineyard, was at last bought in that year; in 1912 it was partly redrained and much of it added to the Mill premises. In 1906 the Apsley Village club and its surrounding land were purchased, and in 1912 part of the Vicarage garden. With this extra land a programme of further building was embarked on. A new power-house was built in 1905, with three generators at work and room for more. In 1907 the Mills were connected to the Hemel Hempstead sewage mains and in 1911 to the system of the National Telephone Co. In 1911 the envelope building (dating from 1900) was extended, the last steam-engine taken out[1] and a motor put in at the end of the year, the van and carriage horses, carts and carriages sold off,[2] the stables converted into a garage, and three cars[3] and a small fleet of vans bought. The transport of work-people was facilitated by a motor bus service run by the L.N.W.R. between Boxmoor and Watford.

The census of 1904 shows Apsley as employing 1,283 work-people and 209 clerical staff; by 1907, these had risen to 1,470 and 293. In 1911 the figures were 1,658 and 304; and in 1914, 2,065 and 477.

The postcard trade greatly developed.[4] Printing was introduced in the Card Department in 1905, for the production of fancy cards, and lithographic printing was started in the Book

[1] Stephenson's horizontal engine, built at Nash Mills, and put up for No. 1 machine in 1860.

[2] A wagonette and a bay mare had been bought as lately as January 1908.

[3] A 16-h.p. Adams landaulette, £443; a 20-h.p. Brasier open car, £90 second-hand, and a 18/24-h.p. Austin limousine, £210 second-hand.

[4] Over 800 million postcards were sent in the United Kingdom in 1905–6.

Department in 1909. In 1904 the Office Equipment Department was initiated with the introduction of a card index from America. Experiments with this and loose-leaf account books were carried out in the Mills themselves. In February 1907 the Managers' Meeting resolved: 'That it is desirable in the interest of Apsley Mill both with a view to internal administrative economies and also in order to increase our book and card trades that we should continue and further develop the use of Loose-leaf Ledgers and books in the Apsley Office, and that the Secretary be requested to communicate with the Auditors so that they may make [the necessary] arrangements.'[1] By 1911 filing cabinets were being made in the book department for office use.

In 1909 F. G. Hawdon was appointed Manager of the Envelope and Stationery Departments. The latter was, indeed, organized as a separate department under his direction in the ensuing year. By 1913 it had a building of its own, and was as autonomous as the older envelope, card and book departments. The demand for matching paper and envelopes in relatively small quantities was met by the production of great quantities of stationery cabinets from the new department.

In 1906 the Hertfordshire Hart had been adopted as the general trade mark of the Upper Mills organization. In 1910 Lion Brand (already used for the export trade)[2] took its place, and remains the hall-mark of Dickinson manufacture. Its introduction coincided with the introduction of the 'Red Sample box' for envelopes, which did much to introduce Apsley envelopes into printers' and stationery shops of Britain.

Nash Mills, shorn of its engineering department, was more and more overshadowed by Apsley, but was developed as a mill for manufacturing pulp board. Its precautions against fire were

---

[1] The card index system had been started at Croxley in 1905.

[2] See p. 131. In August 1907 action was taken against another firm for infringing the Lion trade mark. Earlier action had been taken in 1889 and 1897.

improved in 1903 by an underground fire-main completely enclosing the mill buildings, together with a Shand Mason pump capable of throwing 2,500 gallons per hour. In 1906 Sir John Evans and his household left Nash House[1] which was turned into offices. In 1906 three new Tower beaters were put into the Mill and No. 2 machine was converted into a Triplex machine, the drive being altered to the Cone system in the following year. Eight drying-cylinders were added to this machine four years later, when two more beaters were put in. The old stables and laundry were pulled down, and in May 1908 a new main engine-house was begun. The engine—a Pollitt and Wigzell steam tandem compound horizontal condensing engine of 450 horse-power—was started by young John Dickinson Evans, Lewis Evans's only son, in March 1909. The engine drove all the machinery in the beater-house and salle from a 5-inch steel shaft running below the floor.

By the following year the weekly tonnage had risen to nearly 100 tons, working from 6 a.m. Monday until midnight the following Saturday, and in March 1911 a record of 106 tons in one week was made. At this time, indeed, Nash was the largest maker of white and tinted pulp board in the country, and the only mill wholly devoted to its manufacture. In 1911 the trees in the back yard were cut down, the weir changed, and a new coal wharf, with a capacity of 3,000 tons, made. In June 1911 two old buildings in the centre of the mill were demolished to make room for a three-storey building for paper storage, with an electric lift and loading and unloading facilities. In 1912 the mill was lit by electric light from its own plant. At the end of the year the boiler-house was considerably improved

---

[1] He died on 31 May 1908 at his new home, Britwell, Berkhamsted, now the Technical College of Messrs. Cooper, McDougall and Robertson, Ltd. John Dickinson's grandson, Tom Dickinson, died on 28 October of that year, and John Evans's eldest son Arthur inherited Abbot's Hill but never resided there.

and a new Lancashire boiler with Meldrum mechanical stoker was installed, to bring the battery up to four. In 1913, John William Peacock, the Factory Manager, a member of a family that had served the firm through many generations, patented a strainer—the Dickinson strainer—and one was installed to serve No. 2 machine. Its feature was a rotating drum composed of slatted plates immersed in a vat of pulp, the stuff being drawn into the drum by the pump-like action of discs moving to and fro on a shaft inside the drum. Later, this strainer was fitted to No. 1 machine and worked well for many years.

Home Park, the third of the Upper Mills, started the new century under happy auspices. From 1903 onwards there was a great increase in the demand for art boards for picture postcards. The boom lasted for three or four years; the English Mills were then undersold for a time by the German, but gradually recovered. From June 1905 to May 1906, a second experiment was made in running Home Park night and day. 'The conclusion arrived at', says the Mill Diary, 'was that night work to be successful depends on a double supervisory staff of equal efficiency, and the obtaining of business of a character similar to that found to be most satisfactory when running day staff only, i.e. a recognized proportion of Boards and Papers.'

H. Goldstraw, who had joined the firm in 1896, became Manager in 1909, with Morgan Skeins as Office Manager. In 1913 the freehold of the Mill, which had remained in the Evans family, was bought by the Company for £15,000. It was a good year for the Mill; progress was made in 'velvet finish' and in proofing chromo papers, and the sales were over £100,000.

Croxley was much less fortunate: the Mill made a loss every year from 1906 to 1909, and in 1913. The century had begun well with a growing demand all over the world for Croxley Manifest Bank, but £15,000 for expansion was refused by the Board. Only a few hundreds were allotted every year, except for some £6,500 in 1903. In October 1906, however, C. Barton

Smith brought forward a detailed scheme for increasing the manufacture of 'Croxley Art' by duplicating and triplicating the existing plant. The principle was agreed, and the Board decided to erect the No. 7 paper-machine. At the same time a complete survey of the supply of power to the Mill was made with a view to its electrification. As a consequence a new power-house was built in 1908, with two 750 kw straight condensing Parsons turbo generators. It was a pioneer installation to run at 3,000 revolutions a minute, and proved completely satisfactory. The new No. 7 engine and some of the beaters were also supplied with A.C. beaters. The whole plant was started in March 1908; its success led to the further electrification of the Mill in 1910 and 1912.[1] By 1913 £40,000 had been spent on electrification.

In 1908 the first linen-facing of paper on a plate-glazing machine was accomplished at the Mill, on a plan worked out by John Wilson, the paper-making foreman, and Alfred Green. In 1909 the first cold-milling machine started, followed by a second one a year later. These necessitated an extension of the building and the installation of an air-conditioning plant, completed in 1913, to regulate temperature and humidity. In 1913 the third tub-sizer and air-dryer was installed, and in 1914 the first Duplex cutter was introduced. At the beginning of 1913 Edward Barrs was appointed Consulting Engineer.

In 1911 Croxley tried to make pulp with cotton roots and stalks from Egypt, but the experiment was a failure. In 1913 the experiment was made of working three shifts, each of eight hours. It was found to cause waste, because inexperienced workmen had to be employed; at the end of six months a heavy drop both in quality and output was evident. On 18 February 1914 the Board Meeting minutes recorded: 'Owing to the unsatisfactory financial result of working on Eight Hour shifts during the past year, and the serious difficulty experienced in keeping

[1] The old main engine finally stopped in September and November 1914.

176

the Mill running full time on suitable papers when trade is falling off it has been decided to go back to the old system of Twelve Hour Shifts after Saturday Feb. 21st, running the Mill from 6 am on Monday till 6 pm on Saturday till further notice.'

As a further measure an agreement on the sale of notepaper was entered into between Croxley and Apsley to avoid wasteful competition, and it was arranged[1] that the Croxley and London country sales staff should be amalgamated.

The Dickinson Institute at Croxley was regarded with proprietary affection by C. Barton Smith. In 1900 he tried to get some £2,000 out of the Board for its extension, but failed. Extra rooms were provided by the Centenary gift at a cost of some £1,000 and a games room added in 1910. Outside lecturers, such as Clayton Beadle and R. W. Sindall, lectured there on paper-making, and Lewis Evans on the history of the craft. In 1911 the Institute's amenities were increased by the taking of six acres of ground for a recreation field.

[1] 10 June 1914.

XIII

THE FIRST WORLD WAR

1914–1918

THE WAR of 1914 came with a shock of surprise to Dickinson's, as to most of England. When war was declared on 4 August, the Chairman, Lewis Evans, was also High Sheriff of Hertfordshire and had much to do. Ten days later a notice was issued in every office and mill of the firm:

'THE WAR

'Messrs. John Dickinson & Co. Ld. feel that it is their chief duty to endeavour to keep their works going; subject to this they desire to *urge the men in their employment to enlist in His Majesty's Forces.*

'But as it is not in the best interests of our Country that any should have leave whose absence will stop the work of others, all who desire to enlist should first consult the foreman of their department.

'Places will be kept open for all who leave with the consent of the Company.

'Half wages will be given to all who are married or who have dependents, and one quarter wages to all unmarried men, and a bonus of one month's wages or salary will be given to all those who return at the end of the war.

LEWIS EVANS

Chairman.

God Save the King.'

A week later these privileges were extended to the Reservists, Territorials and Ambulance men who had been called up.[1]

[1] By 1918 the firm was also paying £1 a month through the Prisoners of War Comforts Fund for each employee who was then a prisoner.

Among the Directors Reginald Bonsor, as an officer of the Reserve, was called up at the outbreak of war; Robert Pratt Barlow joined the army as a volunteer. The Home Park Mill Diary records (and it was true of all the Mills): 'Our men went so willingly that it was rather a question of restraining indispensable men from volunteering than of urging any of our men to go . . . The retreat from Mons had its effect on our men as on the whole of our countrymen and reverses only increased the number of those who felt it their duty to enlist.'

In November 1915 Lord Derby's scheme of recruiting came into force, and the same financial aid was granted to those called up under it as to those called up at the beginning of the war. By 1917 some 1,500 men had joined the army from the Mills and offices, of whom 130 had been killed. When the War Memorial was erected at Apsley in 1922 it recorded the names of 225 men who had died among the 1,604 who had enlisted.[1]

The Board early joined the industrialists of England in contributing to the many national and local funds. In August 1914 they voted £250 to the Prince of Wales's Relief Fund, and £20 to the Belgian Relief Fund; in October £100 to Lord Roberts's Indian Fund and £50 to the Fund of the Governor General of South Africa; and similar contributions continued through the war years. Before the end of 1914, 50,000 packets of notepaper, envelopes, postcards and pencils had been dispatched as gifts to the troops.

John Dickinson's, like every other firm in Britain, was soon confronted by a great shortage of labour. There was no official control, and consequently much leakage to highly paid munition making. Much unskilled labour had to be employed, and this dilution caused a great strain on the skilled men who remained in the industry. At Apsley, for example, part of the Mills was commandeered at the beginning of the war for Government

[1] On Christmas Eve 1918, the Board subscribed £1,000 to the Watford War Memorial Hospital.

supplies, and eventually the whole passed under the technical control of the Ministry of Munitions. All through the war measures had continually to be devised to meet emergencies. At most of the Mills little expansion or building was possible; at Apsley, only a canteen, and that just before hostilities ceased.

At Nash Mills overtime was worked on trench bombs and small shells. As far as possible, girls did the work of men. The Manager of Nash Mills was able to say that the women and girls who did the whole of the preparatory work there, as far as the beaters, did it 'just as efficiently as men'. Almost the whole of the Representatives were on active service and their places were taken by a team of 'Sales Ladies' who depended for their contact with the trade on sales and shows held, as stocks were available, in various parts of the country. The shortage of man-power inevitably brought difficulties over hours and rates of pay, intensified by the competition of the government munition factories.

Wages were raised at Home Park in February 1915 on a flexible basis of tonnage, dividing men into two grades of skill. In April the National Union of Paper Workers sent down an organizing secretary to the Mills, who held innumerable meetings at Apsley, Nash and Home Park. Many workers at Nash and Home Park signed on, and some sections (not including envelope workers) at Apsley.

The firm adopted a policy of non-interference. In June the Union formally approached them with demands for increased pay and lessened hours of labour. The Secretary replied that relations for over a century had been of the best, and that the firm was not prepared to accept the Union's intervention. The Chairman issued a card to each worker pointing out that the Company did not belong to any employers' association for controlling labour conditions and wages. All its employees were free to join any Trade Union or Friendly Society, but in view of the firm's long record of happy relations with its employees, it would only discuss questions of wages, hours and conditions of labour with those in its employment who were actually affected by the matters in question.

At the beginning of the Union's campaign Ling had been dead against recognition, even if this attitude were to involve the mills in a strike. Three of the Managers were in favour of recognition of the Union, four were against it. No man, however, was more sensitive than Ling to the public opinion of the men he employed, or more apt to modify his policy to meet it. He knew that there had been the threat of a strike at Croxley and Nash Mills over late working on Saturdays, and had come to believe that recognition must be given to the Union if strikes were to be avoided. On 28 June he therefore sent the Managers a letter advising recognition, followed by a week-end conference at which he converted three of those who were against it.

On 14 July Evans, as Chairman, received a letter from the General Secretary of the National Union of Paper Workers, reporting that mass meetings at the mills had reaffirmed the workers' determination to negotiate for improved wages and working conditions through Union officials. Negotiations followed all through August; Ling, as General Manager of the Upper Mills, Hawdon, as Manager of the Envelope Department at Apsley, and their colleagues, showed both wisdom and initiative in dealing with the questions at issue and serious trouble was avoided.

At Easter 1916 a bonus was given; double wages were paid for a week in July, and a gift was given at Christmas, in compensation for Bank Holidays suspended by Government order. Wages at Home Park were twice raised in the first seven months of 1917, and in September a new policy of war bonuses was instituted for all the employees of the Upper Mills. In November the two Trade Unions in the paper-making industry demanded that the existing war bonus should be added to the standard rates as a permanent wage.

The Union demands did a good deal to flatten out wage rates in the Mills. Before the war Dickinson's had paid their skilled men highly in relation to the unskilled. The Union demands brought the wages of workers such as fitters' labourers and yard men proportionately higher than those of machine men and beater men.

In September 1918 a fresh difficulty arose because some workers at Apsley came under the Master Printers' Federation agreement on wages, and consequently received a higher bonus than anyone in the other Mills. Hawdon then instituted a further voluntary increase of 5s. a week to all men, 3s. to women, and 2s. to young persons, in all the Upper Mills. A further additional bonus on wages, of 6s. 3d. a week to men, 3s. 6d. to women and youths and 2s. 6d. to girls under sixteen, retrospective to 1 July, was granted in October.

Meanwhile the supplies of raw materials grew scarcer and scarcer, and what there was had in great part to be reserved for Government contracts. Home Park was early affected by the stoppage of supplies of German glue and colours. Before long straw was being regularly used at Croxley to increase the volume of pulp and experiments were made with reeds, nettles and hay sweepings, without much success.

In 1916 wood-pulp and other paper-making materials were rationed and the exportation of waste paper prohibited. In July Lewis Evans was invited to become a member of the Royal Commission set up to regulate the imports of paper and paper-making materials. They eventually fixed ceiling prices for these. Paper, however, reached fabulous prices in the course of being sold from merchant to merchant. On 8 September 1916 a first boiling of Hertfordshire trees for wood-pulp was made in No. 1 machine at Croxley. The trees, mostly spruce, poplar and fir, had been collected from woods near Watford, St. Albans, Gaddesden and Aldenham. They were selected by Alfred Green, who used to spend the evenings going round marking possible trees, which were then bought by negotiation with the owners. Mobile lumber camps were organized, with some mill workers among the hands: when the trees were felled the tops and branches were used for firewood and the trunks hauled to the road and brought to the Mill by tractor. On arrival women barked them by hand, before they were split and fed into disc-knife chippers. The chips passed through a disintegrator and a riddle before going to the boilers. Most of the wood was used without bleaching for low-grade paper, but some poplar and aspen was bleached and blended with straw.

In 1917 supplies grew still scarcer, owing to the German submarine blockade, and Government licences halved the previous allowance of pulp.

In 1916 the British Industries Fair held its exhibition in the Victoria and Albert Museum for ten days in February and March. Only samples in cases could be shown, because of shortages; the stand had to be arranged as a reception room. In 1917 only a few special stocks could be shown, and stationers' orders had to be curtailed for the same reason. In 1918 goods had to be rationed to the firm's customers on the basis of their pre-war orders.

Overseas trade was affected in many ways by war conditions. In October 1916 the Board adopted regulations to prevent their foreign factories from competing with home production. They were to prepare a monthly balance sheet, and to refer all questions to a central office at the Old Bailey. In November 1916 the Montreal branch and the Toronto branch which had been established only ten months before, were sold to J. M. Dent & Sons. A year later the South African[1] and Australian branches were turned into separate subsidiary companies. In October 1918 the Board decided the future policy of the firm in its colonial and foreign trade.

[1] This had shown the large profit of £33,120 in 1917.

1. To establish Branch Factories in all suitable quarters of the globe, especially where it is found that the Export trade is not, as a whole, profitable to our Home Mills.

2. The various Branch Factories to make all they can, supplementing their products with any goods made at the Home Mills as is best for the imperial interests of the Firm.

The year 1914 had shown a satisfactory profit; 1915 showed nearly £118,600, largely on accumulated stock. A dividend of 10 per cent and a bonus of 2 per cent was declared.[1] In 1916 a rising market gave nearly £240,000 profit, with a dividend of 10 per cent and a 5 per cent bonus. In 1917 a lower figure was shown, with nearly £108,000 more paid in profits tax than the year before, but dividend and bonus were maintained. In November 1917 the quotation of the Ordinary shares on the London Stock Exchange resulted in an immediate increase in mobility. In May 1918 it was agreed to capitalize £250,000 undivided profits in one paid up share for every £2 held of Ordinary stock.

A great development took place in October 1918, just before the war ended. On the 14th an agreement was entered into between John Dickinson and Co. and Henry Godfrey, Managing Director of Millington and Sons, for the purchase of their Preference and Ordinary shares for £315,000 4½ per cent Debenture stock and £76,500 Ordinary, to be allotted to the Millington shareholders and Directors.[2]

The firm of Millington had been founded in 1824 by a Huguenot, William Leschallas, as paper dealers and rag merchants. In 1840 he began to manufacture envelopes in Skinner's Yard. In 1852 he was joined by C. S. Millington, who later became the owner of the business with Thomas Hutton, trading

[1] The balance sheet could not be circulated in March as the Excess Profits Tax figures were still under discussion.

[2] Millington's had only seven shareholders. The Debenture shareholders of Dickinson's agreed at a meeting on 15 January 1919 to the increase of the Debenture stock by £165,000 at 4½ per cent.

as Millington and Hutton. Ultimately Millington bought out Hutton, and took his two sons, Charles and Walter, into partnership, changing the style of the firm to Millington and Sons. They were the first manufacturing stationers to cut, fold and pack notepaper into five quire packets, instead of selling it flat in reams. Millington and Sons became a limited company in 1898. Millington's nephew, Percy Parminter, acted as Managing Director until his death in 1916. Under his dynamic leadership the firm secured the sole rights in the first rotary envelope machine to be operated in this country. In 1903 the firm moved its main factory in Southwark and its subsidiary factory in Banner Street, to new premises at Crown Works, Tottenham.[1] By 1914 a battery of scores of rotary machines were there turning out millions of envelopes a week at a faster speed than any factory in the world.

In 1905 Millington's had acquired from the American inventors the United Kingdom rights in 'window' envelopes, and were their only manufacturers. In 1911 they had introduced, under the name of 'Basildon Bond', the first 'bond' notepaper to be marketed at 1s. a unit; it proved an immediate success. Tub-sized, air-dried and with about 30 per cent fine quality rag content, it was remarkably good value. Millington's were, in fact, one of Dickinson's most powerful rivals.

The Chairman of Millington's since its incorporation had been Henry Godfrey, originally the firm's auditor. The business was reorganized in 1908, with outside help. As a consequence of the purchase, two Directors, Henry Godfrey and S. G. Bibby, joined the Board of Dickinson's, the former as Chairman. At the same time Evans, who had been due to retire from the chairmanship in January 1918 but had been asked

---

[1] In 1906 Millington's acquired the business, factory and warehouse of the Willcocks Envelope Company, Barwick Street, Birmingham, which they ran as a subsidiary. A second branch factory was established at Manchester in 1909, and a third at Leeds in 1912.

to stay on, decided to retire on account of declining health;[1] C. H. Thomas, who had been a Director for twenty-five years retired, and was succeeded by R. H. Ling. Rothney had resigned the Secretaryship, after thirty years tenure, in March 1916,[2] and it was thus with a Board in great part reconstituted that Dickinson's faced the problems of peace.

---

[1] He died after many years of ill-health on 25 September 1930.
[2] E. C. Cowdrey was appointed in his place.

XIV

R. H. LING

1918–1926

IN THE years after the First World War the firm of John Dickinson was dominated by a man not of Dickinson blood, who had risen from the ranks. In 1855 Reuben Ling entered the service of Longmans Green and Co.;[1] by 1889 he had risen to be the head of their publishing department. In 1864 his son, Reuben Herbert Ling, was born at Greenwich. When he was fifteen, his father brought him to see Frank Pratt Barlow, whom he knew through his work at Longman's. The quiet and modest Barlow listened with amusement while the boy declared to him his ambition to rise to be the head of any concern he entered; if he took orders (as he then contemplated) he would end as Archbishop of Canterbury. Ling never entered the Church, but Barlow offered him a junior clerkship at the Old Bailey and from clerk's high desk he rose to command the firm of John Dickinson and Company. From 1879 to 1890 he was in the Sales Department at 65 Old Bailey and acquired a sound knowledge of the trade. In 1890 he was appointed Manager at Apsley, and in 1894 had the other two Upper Mills set under his charge. On 1 January 1918 he was appointed a Joint Managing Director. His colleague, Henry Godfrey,[2] concerned himself mainly with the Tottenham factory. On 18 November 1924 Godfrey died suddenly, and the Board

[1] Cox & Chandler, *House of Longman* 1724–1924 (privately printed 1925), p. 85. He retired in 1902.
[2] A. H. Godfrey was elected an Annual Director in 1922 but retired in 1925.

elected Ling Chairman and sole Managing Director.[1] Wemyss resigned, and a financial expert, H. A. Vernet, took his place as Director. F. G. Hawdon, who had been elected an Annual Director in 1922,[2] and Major Bonsor were given specific responsibilities as 'active' Directors. Morgan Skeins and W. E. Ellens were appointed Annual Directors in 1926 and full Directors in 1928, when R. S. Dove, F. Huckle and R. E. Ridgway, of the managerial staff, were appointed Annual Directors. W. C. Jarvis was appointed Secretary to the Company in May 1920.

It is almost impossible to exaggerate the change represented by Ling's appointment. He was a man who had educated himself and had no share in the scientific attainments or in the traditional culture of his predecessors. He had few links with Hertfordshire and played little part in its affairs outside his Mills. His predecessors had seen their manufacture in terms of technique; he saw it in terms of sales promotion and the management of labour. When Croxley Mills first came under his direction, he failed to realize the difference between a paper-mill and a factory for manufacturing stationery, and thought that drive and energy would suffice to increase its production. Morgan Skeins, who knew him well and worked with him long, wrote of him as 'a fighter—full of ambition for himself and the Company he served; with a power over men which was exceptional and with a trader's instinct'.

Ling was, however, a professed idealist—his favourite words were 'uplift' and 'inspiration'—with a strong taste for mottoes and slogans to express his ideals. His predecessors had taken it for granted that paper-making was an honest and honourable way of earning a living; Ling discovered the fact for himself and made a gospel of it.

[1] The appointment of men in the employment of the Company as Annual Directors was considered by the Board on 11 November 1919.
[2] The election was in the first instance for five years.

Ling was a man of strong character, who inspired profound affection or dislike. W. E. Ellens, who worked out the details of his grandiose schemes, admired him greatly; to most of his work-people he was an impressive and sympathetic figure; but there were times when Ling and some of his Managers were hardly on speaking terms.

He did not love the Evanses (his loyalty was given to the Pratt Barlows) and was not a slave to the tradition of the firm. His instructions for a booklet of John Dickinson & Co., dictated soon after his appointment as Managing Director, show his point of view.

'The House of Dickinson—in our type—to be in gold on the cover. Also the "Lion Brand" ... clearly shown in gold ...

'First you have a photograph of the dominant man—Mr. Ling—with his signature underneath.

'Then start with the dominant organization—which is making paper

'A definition of Croxley Mill with a big picture of the "Lion Brand"—and a little photograph of Mr. Skeins and the people who control it—with a definition of the papers made

"Lion Brand" shouting out.

'Then show the interior of the Mill— never mind about the outside.

'A great big interior—showing that we have got more than one machine. Something that gives a vision of the immensity of the Mill ...

'Nothing about John Dickinson and the past—Just "Established 1804".   R.H.L.'

Ling had been appointed sole Managing Director in 1918. By the autumn of 1919 he found himself challenged by a severe trade recession; by September markets were heavy and there was a serious fall in prices. In November a further capital issue of £250,000 shares was contemplated, but in February 1920 it was decided not to capitalize more reserves in view of the general situation. In April the completion of the authorized issue of Ordinary shares was decided on, by the issue of £173,500 to existing shareholders at par, in the proportion of one new share for every five old.

The year 1921 was a year of unprecedented bad trade. Markets were stagnant; stocks fell in value; a coal strike sent up costs; wood pulp was in short supply, and there were difficulties over Indian and other exchange rates. In January Croxley closed down for a week for want of orders: the first 'shut' in the firm's history. The Ordinary dividend, which had remained at 10 per cent with a 5 per cent bonus, was cut to 7½ per cent.

In May it was reported that the authorized capital expenditure of £180,000 and the taxation liabilities of £330,000 would necessitate releasing funds locked up in overseas branches. A more minute system of costing was adopted, and by the autumn conditions were improving. Ling started an economy campaign and a production drive. The next few years saw improving conditions; it was found possible to maintain the dividend at 10 per cent.[1]

General progress in all main departments was reported in 1926. The decision was made in October of that year to issue £250,000 new Ordinary shares to the existing shareholders at a percentage below the current market value.

In February 1919 an Administrative Board, with the Managing Director as Chairman, was set up to deal with technical details. By 1920–1 the greater number of the Directors'

[1] A bonus of 1½ per cent was given in 1927 and of 2½ per cent in 1928.

decisions on financial, engineering, welfare and marketing questions were made by approval of resolutions passed by the
Administrative Board.

The pre-war policy of developing the Mills bore good fruit
in the years after the war, when building costs were high. At
the same time further changes were made, particularly at
Apsley. In 1922 a new Power House was built, which, with its
boilers, steam-turbines and generators, cost £70,000.[1] In 1925
the entrance was reconstructed, with a new Time office,[2] visitors'
room, first-aid room and rest room, and a large new Tag
Department was built. In the following year the Board passed
capital expenditure of £100,000 for pulling down the oldest
part of the Mills[3] and rebuilding the Envelope Department.
The new building was the largest at Apsley, and the first to be
built of reinforced concrete.

In 1919[4] and 1920 the Guildhouse Canteen was built at a
cost of some £11,500, across the road from the Mills. In 1920
its running was costing the firm £3,000 a year. An Efficiency
Training Centre or Works School was set up in the men's old
Canteen, with its own organizer in charge, to give young employees an hour's instruction on every full working day.[5] Office
workers attended until they were sixteen, craft workers for their
first six months. The fairly small classes enabled the teacher and

[1] A new generating engine was added in 1925.

[2] George Hughes, the time-keeper for thirty-nine years, and member of the Fire Brigade for thirty-five (and finally Chief Officer) retired
in 1926 at the age sixty-five.

[3] The last of John Dickinson's original water-wheels was removed in
the process.

[4] The contract, for £7,281, was signed on 23 October 1918.
Throughout the war the firm paid an annual grant of £75 to the
Canteen.

[5] It had been started in 1918 under Frank Clark, who had about
fifty pupils, and was reorganized under W. J. Newell in 1923, 1933
and 1939. It came to an end with the Second World War.

the lecturers (mostly from the Mills) to gain some knowledge of the potentialities of the young entry.

The chief changes at Apsley were in general organization, which was further concentrated there. In 1919 the firm's selling organization was split into two teams: one of representatives for the Paper and Board Mills, and another for Apsley.[1] In 1921 the Croxley Counting House was transferred to Apsley. In 1923 a special service of office, despatch and transport was set up to develop the Mill's trade direct with the London customers. The Stationery Department developed the manufacture of writing-pads and 'compendiums' and stationery in fancy boxes to meet post-war fashions. In February 1925 an arrangement was entered into with Mabie Todd & Co. for the sole manufacture of Swan Pen Vellum. A department for typewriting-paper was instituted, in competition with that at Croxley.

Apart from the general development of the manufacturing sections, the other mill activities continued much as before the war. The Fire Brigade won the District Shield at Bletchley, and the Grand Aggregate Shield and a number of other awards at Basingstoke in 1922. The Grand Aggregate Shield and eight other awards were won in 1923. Croxley (the other Dickinson Brigade) won the Grand Aggregate Shield in 1924, and Apsley in 1925 and 1929.

Nash Mills had been less fully developed than Apsley before the war, and found itself handicapped by insufficient room and inadequate plant in the Salle and Finishing department. By 1922 it was consistently receiving more orders than it could execute, in spite of modernization of the press rolls and No. 2 machine. In that year various experiments were made with the Dickinson 'making' cylinder, of which the principle had been in part forgotten, and finally No. 1 machine was running five cylinders of the old design.

---

[1] The two organizations were again merged in 1951.

Late in 1926 a plan of general improvements was adopted. New stores for raw materials, waste paper and wood pulp were built on the opposite side of the Mill, with a system of belts on which waste could be sorted. A new machine was ordered in 1928, and the beater-house was remodelled, with an additional storey. The Mill kept at work through it all.

C. Barton Smith retired from the managership of Croxley at the end of 1918, after forty-eight years with the firm,[1] and it was united with the Upper Mills under Ling's general direction. Albert Butler came from Nash to take over Croxley under him, and Goldstraw came to Nash Mills after twenty-three years at Home Park. Albert Butler retired three years later and was succeeded by Morgan Skeins. On 22 May 1924 the most serious fire in the history of the firm broke out in the main office building at Croxley, spreading to the stock-rooms and stationery department. In spite of the valiant efforts of the Croxley and Apsley Fire Brigades, the damage was assessed at over £55,000. No great scheme of reorganization resulted, but the damaged buildings were reconstructed.

The chief development at the time lay in machinery. In 1924 Croxley put in its No. 1 paper-making machine (completely rebuilt in 1954) to supersede one of forty-two years' service, and six years later installed its No. 4 (now No. 3), having a deckle of 110 inches and a capacity of 100 tons per week. No. 2 was a narrow machine, used chiefly for linen-faced papers. No. 3 machine was a Dickinson cylinder machine built in 1840–1, used to make exceptionally fine book papers. The other remarkable machine was No. 7, started in 1908, which made extra-strong thin papers. The Mill at that time specialized in relatively small quantities of good quality and, for the most part, branded papers.

The trend of the market was towards the mass-production of

[1] In one of the Rooms at the Croxley Institute is a bronze plaque to the memory of 'Charles Barton Smith, 1854–1929. Founder of the Institute.'

writing- and printing-paper, and in 1926 it was decided to modernize the Mill at a cost of some £142,000 in the ensuing years.[1]

The lectures on paper-making which had long been included in the programme of the Croxley Institute were put on a more systematic basis, with a view to some of the students taking the paper-making examinations of the City and Guilds Institute.

In 1919 the Board decided to sell the London premises at Upper Thames Street and Paul's Wharf;[2] in 1920 the lease of 56 Ludgate Hill was terminated by the owners. The Board decided in 1921 to rebuild the inside of 65 Old Bailey at a cost of some £108,000, leaving the 1871 façade almost intact.[3] The Paddington Wharf continued in use for canal traffic, though road transport was being developed; in 1925 over 13,000 tons of stuff was dealt with there.

Little change was made in the provincial organization. In 1920 a small factory for special orders was set up in Bristol,[4] the building in Queen Street, Manchester, was improved, and new premises were acquired at Newcastle. In 1925 it was decided to sell the Belfast premises and the equipment and good-will of the box-making factory that had been developed to cater for the Irish Linen trade.

Little attempt was made at this time to integrate Millington's into the Dickinson organization. The Millington business remained practically autonomous, and as late as 1925 built a new label factory to compete with Apsley. Their London office, which since the foundation of the Company had been in Budge Row, was in 1925 transferred to 1 Amen Corner. Basildon Bond steadily increased in popularity, stimulated by an advertising campaign authorized in 1924.

[1] See p. 209.
[2] The sale was effected for £11,000 in October 1922.
[3] A House Council for the offices was set up in 1921, to discuss matters of common interest to its departments.
[4] At first in John Street; after 1924 in Fairfax Street.

The whole question of export trade received much attention from the Board, though for some time conditions varied so quickly that no settled policy was achieved. In December 1919 the Board gave some consideration to the registration of a local company in India. Further consideration was given to the question of local companies in January 1921, when the Chairman was asked to visit the overseas branches to investigate the possibilities. In April local companies in Australia and New Zealand were authorized. Six months earlier an Export Council of Direction, consisting of Hawdon, Gill and Ellens, had been set up to direct the work from England. Ling rechristened the Export department of the Old Bailey the Imperial Department, and in 1924 it was drastically reorganized under Hawdon.

The Eastern branches had some notable ups and downs. A site for a factory at Kamarhatti, near Calcutta, was acquired in March 1919, and a factory and godowns were built there in 1922. In 1924 the Indian organization was reconsidered with a view to its autonomy, but the times proved unfavourable. In July 1926 its branches were again reorganized under Hawdon, who went out to India for the purpose,[1] and Kamarhatti was closed down. The branches were put under their own managers, directly responsible to the Mills, which in their turn took over responsibility from the Old Bailey. The Rangoon branch was closed; the Penang office was moved to Singapore at the end of 1922, and the Shanghai branch was reconstructed in 1926. The Cairo office was temporarily discontinued in 1925, but was later reopened under the Management of W. H. Millwood.

Those responsible for the development of the firm's business in Australia had long been pressing for the establishment of a local factory, of which the products would not be liable to the heavy tariffs operating against English manufactures. The firm, however, at that time felt that their capital was needed at home.

[1] He returned to England in April 1927 and again took up his position as Export Manager.

Ultimately Snashalls Ltd. of Sydney was purchased in 1920 to provide a headquarters and factory for the Australian branch. It had been a personally conducted business, and proved less successful than the Board had hoped. Two years later J. W. Timberlake was sent there from South Africa with considerable powers, in order to organize the new concern. He was followed in 1925 by F. G. Hawdon, R. E. Ridgway, the Stationery Department Manager, and G. D. Collins, the Mills' Accountant.[1] They advised the enlargement of the premises in Bellevue Street, Sydney, to provide a combined factory and warehouse. The old Snashall plant was replaced by modern machinery, and the printed-envelope department developed.

A small office had been opened in Wellington to deal with the New Zealand trade not long before the war, but it then came under the Australian branch. In 1920 a New Zealand manager, H. J. Tubbs, was appointed direct from Apsley Mills, and in 1921 an Auckland warehouse was instituted under C. G. Tripp, an Apsley man who had earlier migrated to New Zealand. The slump of 1921–2 coincided with the development of the branch, and it ran at a loss for a time. A factory was opened in Wakefield Street, Wellington, in 1923, to make the simpler kinds of manufactured stationery against which a heavy tariff operated. In 1927 Croxley House, Wellington, was built; it was at first mainly intended for envelope manufacture.

These experiences resulted in the Board's formulating an Overseas trading policy towards the end of 1925. The Directors recognized that times had changed from the days when their task had been simply to supply a market for which there was no local competition. The new policy of developing local factories to avoid tariff barriers might create a wasteful competition between their products and those of the Hertfordshire Mills,

[1] The Board Meeting of 10 March 1925 allocated some £60,000 from General Reserves towards setting the Australasian Company on a new footing.

and a new policy must be adopted by which the overseas branches sold the firm's English products and their own with as little competition as possible. For paper and boards, in particular, it was decided that they were to be stockists only.

The chief problem of the time, and the chief development, lay in the firm's relation with its work-people. In 1919 high prices produced constant demands for higher wages and shorter hours, which received Government support. The Government, indeed, declared that it was its wish that every employer should be in a Federation and every worker in a Union. Ling did all that he could to promote both ideas: Goldstraw was sent round the mills of other firms to encourage them to join the Employers' Federation and the Mill managers were ordered to appear on the platform at meetings with Union representatives, and to recommend workers to join. As early as 21 January 1919 J. Burles (representing the management) was authorized to sign a notice of agreement between the firm and the National Union of Printing and Paper Workers, applying to the three Upper Mills.[1] By this a week's notice on either side, or a week's pay in lieu of notice, was agreed to, and collections for the Union were authorized once a week, each room having its own re-cognized collector. Soon afterwards, a forty-eight-hour week was adopted for day-workers, who had been working from fifty-four to forty-eight hours, and shift-workers were put on three shifts to give an average forty-four hour week, the weekly rotation being fifty-two, forty and forty hours, one shift in four having Saturday off.

In the years between the wars the Directors gave much thought to the question of strengthening the relations with staff and work-people. At the Board Meeting of 9 December 1919 it was decided that employees should have the opportunity of subscribing to the Firm's coming issue of shares. In July 1920 the issue was recommended, with the proviso that a private Trust

[1] It was shortly extended to cover Croxley also.

Company should be formed to buy back the shares when an employee left the Company or wished to sell for other reasons. On the profits for the year a Pension Fund of £50,000 was started. In 1925 a limit of £1,000 was set on any one person's holding of Employees' shares. When in 1928 £250,000 Employees' shares were issued (together with a similar amount of Ordinary shares) it was agreed that their holders should not be allowed to sell them except to their Trust.

On 19 January 1920 it was agreed to reduce the hours to forty-four a week, without reduction of pay. On 18 May the Chairman reported that the Federation of Master Printers had offered an increase of 6s. a week to men and 2s. 6d. to women, which had been refused by the Unions; and proposals for reference to arbitration in the Industrial Court had been rejected. It was recognized that the situation was grave, and daily conferences were held. In July machine men were granted 2s. an hour for the forty-four hour week and unskilled day-workers 1s. 5¾d. an hour for a forty-eight hour week.

By October 1920 the slump had set in and short time was being worked at Apsley. In December the Administrative Board set £500 aside for workers who 'by reason of the present slackness existing in the Mills are in real distress'.

In January 1921 the Master Printers' Federation granted 5s. a week to men and 2s. to women, and a similar increase was under consideration on a demand to the Employers' Federation of Envelope Makers. The slump and the national coal strike postponed the question; and on 6 December 1921 the Administrative Board decided that no advances or reductions in salaries or wages should be considered, except in cases of very special merit or heavily increased responsibility: the decision remained in force until November 1923. In October 1922 retiring allowances based on an annual charge of 5 per cent on the salaries of non-operative staff in the United Kingdom were recommended. In May 1925 a week's holiday with pay was granted to the employees of all four Mills, to be 'staggered' to avoid closing the Mills; financial assistance up to half fees was granted to employees selected by the General Managers for education, and £1,027 was allowed for dinners, socials and other entertainments for employees. In July 1925 it was agreed that full salary should be paid to members of the managerial and clerical staff for three months if they were absent for sickness and the circumstances warranted it.

In the spring of 1926 the pace quickened. On 20 April the Administrative Board considered an award of the Industrial Court, which gave an increase of about ½d. an hour in paper-mills. On 30 April the Government subsidy to the coal-mines came to an end, and rather than accept reduced pay or increased hours the miners decided to strike. On 3 May their action was followed by a General Strike of key industries throughout the country, called by the T.U.C. They called out the printers in order to paralyse the news service, and the paper-makers, whose union was linked with that of the printers, came out too. On that day the Board had a notice posted in all the Mills: 'We wish to inform our workers that during the present crisis our aim at Mills and Branches will be to provide employment as long as circumstances permit.' That afternoon the Shop Stewards met the Managers to tell them that work would cease that evening. Cease it did, and the factories at Apsley, Nash, Home Park, Croxley, Sumner Street and Tottenham closed down. Extra night-watchmen were put on duty, and special constables enrolled.

On 7 May a circular was posted to every worker, with a copy of the Government proclamation by which protection was promised to all who returned to work, to say that the Mills would reopen on Saturday, 8 May. On that day 178 workers turned up at Apsley, although the road to the Mills was strongly picketed.

Ling had had for a long time a scheme in mind that should

fully express his view of Dickinson's as 'a united family, work-ing with unselfish devotion for the common good, governed by a Stewardship that secures for all the just reward of their labour'. He knew, too, that he had his Directors behind him. The crisis of the General Strike precipitated the formulation of the scheme, for in it they saw a fundamental solution of the current difficulties.

On Saturday, 8 May, Ling, the Mill Directors and the Managers conferred together all day. On Sunday their discus-sions continued.[1] That night a circular was posted to all workers to say that no distinction would be made between trade unionists and non-unionists. At 12.30 on Wednesday, 12 May, the T.U.C. called off the General Strike, though the coal strike continued. Ellens, in a speech to workers and strikers at Apsley, made it clear that a Union of the House of Dickinson was being set up in place of an outside union. Similar announcements were made in the other Mills.

On 13 May meetings of workers were held at which the Union of the House of Dickinson was explained. Enrolment forms were distributed on the 15th and returned, without excep-tion, duly filled up on the 17th. On that day it was agreed that an interim subscription should be levied on the basis of the old Union dues. On 20 May the Administrative Board approved the charter of the Union, which was passed by the Board of Directors on 25 May. They then allocated £50,000 of Special Reserve which remained invested in the Company at 5 per cent to start a Benefit Fund, and gave £5,000 similarly invested to the Union for the relief of special cases of distress. On 22 June

---

[1] So urgently did Ling present the whole necessity for speed that when he was told that an Actuary who had been approached with regard to formulating a pension scheme had said he would need a month or so to prepare the details, Ling insisted on its production within forty-eight hours, and was successful in seeing his determination bring the outline of the scheme to him within the desired time.

a Committee of Management and provisional sub-committees were elected. On 29 June a Trust Fund was created of £100,000 for meeting the pension obligations of the Union, to be filled by a charge of 2½ per cent on manual workers' wages and a contribution from profit.

The rules and regulations of the new Union were issued in August with effect from 1 September. They laid down that all employees, including Craft Workers, Staff Workers and Directors, should be Members of the Union. No strikes or lock-outs would be sanctioned, but it should be an object of the Union to secure conditions that would enable its workers to earn more than the minimum Trade Union rates. A Guild of Sport should be formed. Medical attention should be given and convalescent accommodation provided, and funds for sickness and unemployment benefits, payments at death, and a pensions fund set up. The firm were to bear the costs of administration, leaving all subscriptions available for benefits.

A special section of the Charter promised Craft Workers that their wages should not fall below recognized Trade Union standards, and that piece-work rates should not be reduced except when some mechanical development or other improvement automatically increased the production. They were promised hours not longer than those worked in the trade generally, a week's paid holiday and (after 1 January 1938) pensions at sixty-five ranging from 32s. 6d. to 22s. 6d. based on contributions of from 2s. to 1s. a week, according to age and wages earned, with proportionate benefits if they retired between sixty and sixty-five, or had not subscribed for forty years. Women were to receive full pension benefit at a lower rate of 17s. 6d. at sixty. Sickness, unemployment and death payments were provided for; and a woman member resigning on marriage was to receive back her accumulated payments as a dowry.

Staff workers received a fortnight's holiday and comparable benefits, with a contribution ranging from 2½ per cent to 5 per cent of their salary, balanced by a payment from the firm of $2\frac{1}{2}$ per cent of the aggregate current salaries, with a normal retiring age of sixty.

By November 1926 Ling was able to say that 'The organization for sick visiting and the prompt action in all cases where help was needed was strengthening the human link and cementing all in the ideals of our Union'. The Union of the House of Dickinson remains the most impressive monument of his direction of the Mills; it still uses the best-remembered slogan of his time: 'A Light to the End of the Road.'

XV

BEFORE THE WAR
1927–1939

IN MAY 1927 R. H. Ling suffered a severe breakdown in
health, and was ordered a complete rest.[1] He went on a long
voyage in September, and did not attend a Board Meeting
until 12 June 1928. In December 1928 he went off on another
voyage, returning to work at Easter 1929. In December he
resigned, after fifty years' service with the firm.[2]

F. G. Hawdon was appointed Chairman and Managing
Director, with Skeins, Ellens and Dove as working Directors.
Robert Pratt Barlow had resigned his Directorship, and gone
to live in Sicily, in 1928; his departure severed the last link
between the firm's administration and the Dickinson family.
H. A. Vernet, who had brought considerable financial acumen
to the Board table, died after a short illness in 1933.

F. G. Hawdon had joined the firm in 1897. Six months later
he had been appointed Manager of Home Park. In 1909 he had
been transferred to the Envelope Department at Apsley. In
1918 he had become General Manager; in 1922 he became an
Annual Director, and a full Director in 1925. After the war he
had been sent to inspect and where necessary reorganize the
Company's overseas branches. He had therefore a notably wide
experience of the Company's activities, both on the manufacturing and selling side. Skeins, who knew him well and worked

[1] Sir Reginald Bonsor was appointed Deputy Chairman and F. G.
Hawdon, who had just returned from India, Deputy Managing
Director.
[2] He died on 15 March 1939.

with him long, wrote that never had there been two men so different in temperament and outlook as Ling and Hawdon. Hawdon, he considered, was 'one who was by nature a teacher; one who took joy in all the beautiful things of life—in whose judgement those things which were spiritual carried much greater weight than more material things'. Another colleague wrote of him as 'a maker of men'.

His gifts of co-ordination and friendship promised the peaceful development which the Mills needed, and the promise was being fulfilled when, on 12 June 1933, he died suddenly and unexpectedly. He was greatly mourned and long regretted.

Sir Reginald Bonsor (who had succeeded to his father's Baronetcy in 1929) had for some time been the senior Director on the Board, but with characteristic modesty and good sense had three times stood down from election to the Chairmanship in favour of Godfrey, Ling and Hawdon, successively, since he considered that their appointments were in the Firm's interest. On Hawdon's death he was appointed Chairman: a position which he held until 1955. Skeins was appointed Managing Director for paper and boards, Ellens for envelopes and manufactured stationery, and Dove for export. Ellens resigned for reasons of health at the end of 1936, while retaining a seat on the Board; Skeins then took over the Managership of the whole Home organization and moved his office from Croxley to Apsley. In 1936 J. W. Randall, who had been Secretary to the Company since 1928, was appointed Financial Director, and T. W. Shearman took his place as Secretary.

In October 1928 the registered offices of the Company, under the new Secretary J. W. Randall, had been transferred from the Old Bailey to Apsley, and by 1936 the whole financial organization was centred at Apsley, with a mechanical accounting system on the punched-card system in the financial department.

In 1930 a general slump overtook the trade of Great Britain.

Profits and dividends were reduced in that and subsequent years, and only recovered five years later.

In 1931 the integration of Millington's into the Dickinson organization was begun; it was completed in the autumn of 1932. The tag label department was transferred from Apsley to Tottenham, to avoid wasteful competition, and 'Basildon Bond' was transferred from Tottenham to Apsley, together with the envelope office staff. Mass-produced envelopes, however, continued to be manufactured at Tottenham, while the Apsley machines were concentrated on specialized production. The two selling organizations were merged on 1 October 1932, with Apsley as the centre for despatches and correspondence.

The trade depression continued. In June 1932 serious consideration was given to the question of a reduction in wages and salaries to Craft and Staff workers. More emphasis was put on sales organization, and further departmental competition eliminated. New sorts of paper and uses for it were found, from special linen-faced boards for the making of paper clerical collars, to specially ruled betting calculators and specially absorbent paper mats for beer-mugs.

A crisis in the trade began in October 1936 with a great shortage of wood pulp. John Dickinson and Co. kept prices as stable as possible, but in April 1937 had to increase listed prices by 5 per cent. In that year, however, it was found possible at the Converting Mills to reduce hours from forty-eight to forty-five a week, and to adopt a five-day week, with no reduction in wages.

The firm's policy on advertising and presentation of its products gradually became more standardized. In 1927 the Administrative Board agreed to stress the use of 'Lion Brand' on all the firm's products. In 1928 £10,000 was voted to start an advertising campaign for 'Lion Brand'; among other things a travelling showroom was set up in an elegant van to tour round Britain. A series of further campaigns began in 1929. In 1932 'Basildon Bond' proved itself the best-selling notepaper in the

United Kingdom; its position was confirmed by an advertising campaign in 1934.

In 1927 an old part of Apsley Mill was demolished and a new envelope building erected on the site.[1] The top floor was devoted to the making of high-grade Court and small commercial envelopes, the third to ordinary 'bankers'' envelopes, and the second to bag-shaped envelopes. The first floor housed the printing plant, and the ground floor machinery, a box-making plant, and a stock-room. In March 1933 the Mill for the first time reached the production of one hundred million envelopes in a week, with orders for 1,046 million for the quarter between January and March. In September it was decided to add a new wing to the Envelope Department at an estimated cost of £27,000. At the same time the production of the 'Monotuk' envelope for printed matter, designed for ease and speed in closing, brought yet more trade to the Mill. It was followed in 1937 by the use of latex as an adhesive for 'Seal-Easi' envelopes. About 1934 the development of air mail increased the need for lightweight paper and envelopes, and special stationery was manufactured to meet the demand. The sum of £11,000 was approved for a new building for mass-produced stationery in May 1935.[2]

About 1927 part of the original Mill—'The Cottage'—was extended in the same simple architectural style to provide a new Board Room, Directors' and Visitors' dining-rooms, a conference room, and nurse's and first-aid rooms.[3] The new building for the Card Department, which was begun in 1933, was completed

[1] Fresh uses for packaging-envelopes were found at this time, such as sandwich bags, bags for kippers, rashers, bread, shirts and lingerie, and film wallets.

[2] In January 1936 E. G. Parris, who had earlier been General Manager of the Envelope Department, was appointed General Manager of the whole Envelope and Manufacturing Stationery Organization.

[3] A dental clinic was added in 1930. In 1933 the first Medical Officer, Dr. Gilbert Burnett, was appointed.

at a total cost of some £100,000; it covered all that was left of the old 'Salmon' Meadow.

In 1929 storage had to be provided for more than 1,200 bicycles while their owners were at work in the Mill. In 1930 a new factory and office for the Book Department was completed, at a cost of £12,000, and a new photo-lithographic plant installed, and in 1931 a new department for packing supplies such as cellophane bags, wrappings and so on was set up in the building vacated on the removal of the tag factory to Tottenham.[1] The Envelope Department was split into two sections, Pocket and Banker, each on its separate balance sheet, and under its own Manager. More dining space was provided by adding a Staff dining-hall to the Guildhouse;[2] the power-house was enlarged; a new system of transport by tractor and trailer between the Mills and Boxmoor Railway Station was instituted, and part of the canal culverted to provide more quay room for outward traffic.

In 1938 great developments were made in transport. A passenger station was built immediately opposite the Mills, chiefly to meet the needs of the Apsley work-people; it was opened on 28 September 1938 by a special train, with the Chairmen of the L.M.S. and Dickinson's as passengers, which drove through a huge screen of Croxley paper stretched across the rails.

The question of the acquisition of the Longman estate at Shendish had first been raised in 1911.[3] It came up again on the death of Thomas Norton Longman towards the end of 1930. In March 1936 it was bought by the firm, and a committee formed to direct its transformation into a club for the work-people. In May 1937 it was opened by the Chairman, Sir Reginald Bonsor, as the headquarters of the Dickinson

---

[1] In 1936 this was extended on the site of the old Vicarage, the firm building a new Vicarage on the other side of the railway.

[2] £9,500 expenditure was authorized on 27 March 1934.

[3] Board Meeting, 25 January 1911.

Guild of Sport, at a cost to the firm of some £15,000. The house, built in 1854–6, provides an agreeable and handsome Clubhouse, with changing rooms and space for indoor games, and its gardens and park provide grounds for football, cricket, tennis, hockey and bowls, and for a swimming pool. Members of the Union and their wives can become members of the Guild of Sport for a nominal payment.

In March 1927 the Board decided to spend £75,000 at Nash Mills on a large new building for raw materials on the site of the old stables and dairy, with a process bay containing the plant for the preparatory dusting, sorting and pulping. The Mill chimney was demolished. In the following year the beater-house was remodelled, with new beaters, stuff chests and electric gear, and a number of new machines, costing some £130,000, installed. A second new board machine, partly built in the firm's own engineering department, was set up in 1933, raising the normal production to some 180 tons a week. The Salle proved too small for this, and in 1934 a new Salle was built on the site of the old waste sheds. Difficulties over the Mill effluent were met by the installation of a Swedish plant to precipitate the fibre and sizing before the water was returned to the mill-stream. In 1937 Goldstraw retired from Nash Mills; he had known it since the years when he used to hand in Sir John Evans's letters through the dining-room window, and had, during his managership, always kept the old square garden as well tended as it had been in John Dickinson's day. Shortly afterwards a new export packing room and a new canteen were built, and new cutting and drying machinery put in.

In 1927 a parallel reorganization of Home Park was begun. The four coating machines were moved to a new building, and a new drying plant was installed. A new gumming plant was purchased for £7,500 and the manufacture of gummed tape introduced.[1] In 1933 the goodwill of the Dominion Foil Co.

[1] In 1932 there was a development in the manufacture of 'Holdfast' gummed tape at Home Park Mills.

was acquired, and a Foils Department started. A new power plant was installed to enable the whole Mill to be driven electrically. The Mill (always a small one) at this time employed two hundred workers.

Croxley was more profoundly affected by the trade depression than any other of the Mills. In 1927 a new building of reinforced concrete was built, and served by four electric lifts, with a floor-space of 65,000 superficial feet. It provided storage space for over 2,000 tons of paper, with a railway siding running into the stock-room, four hydraulic presses for packing paper for export, and new offices. In the next year a new esparto plant was set up, with boilers designed to deal with 400 tons of raw esparto a week. A new soda recovery plant was also installed. In 1930 (the Centenary of the Mill) all the machinery was electrified, eight new beaters were put into a new beater-house, a rotary vacuum filter was purchased and a new 110-inch paper-machine (No. 4) was set up in a new machine-house, capable of producing 100 tons of paper a week.

Between January and the beginning of July 1928, 5,280 miles of paper from the Croxley reels was turned into books. It is not surprising that when in 1934 the First Edition Club chose the fifty best-produced books of the year, seventeen of them were found to be printed on Croxley paper.

None the less the financial crisis of 1931 hit the Mill hard; it had to be closed for lack of orders for three days in June and six in December.

In 1931 a complete 'white water' system was put in, reducing the amount of usable material lost in the effluent and economizing in water, and in the following year a new borehole was drilled to provide an additional water supply.

In 1932 the Mill laboratory was established under the direction of the work's chemist, Dr. Julius Grant.[1] It has rooms for

[1] He also undertook the paper-making classes at the Dickinson Institute.

optical and microscopical work and paper testing, and laboratories for general chemistry and wet-paper work, with a miniature beater. The laboratory undertakes routine testing at various stages of pulp- and paper-making; investigation into raw materials; the solution of day to day problems in the Mills; and the devising of papers for special purposes.

One of the questions to be solved was that of the Mill effluent. In 1934 the Thames Conservancy brought a case against the firm for pollution; a fine of £20 was imposed, and the Mill was warned that immediate steps must be taken to purify the water leaving the Mill. A new method was worked out and eventually patented.[1] The necessary plant was set up, at a cost of about £17,000, and hourly tests for chlorine were instituted.

In 1933 the question of the general reorganization of the Mill came under consideration, and a policy of further mechanization was adopted, including the pulling out of the then Nos. 2, 3 and 6 machines, and their replacement by two machines, one of 145 inches trimmed width, and one of 110 inches.

The most fruitful development lay in the production of 'Evensyde' paper, which was first put on the market in the summer of 1935. No. 4 machine was fitted with a second wire, arranged to run in the opposite direction. The paper formed on this lower wire and that from the upper were amalgamated immediately in a special press in such a way that the 'wire' sides came together. It was, in fact, a development of the duplex paper that John Dickinson had invented a century before.

The reorganization of the envelope department at Tottenham in 1932, and the shift of a part of the department to Apsley, released a certain amount of factory space in the Tottenham factory. This was occupied in part by a new Karrier Bag Department and in part by the transfer (made in 1934) of the Household Stationery Department from Apsley. Three years later the Tottenham factory was enlarged at a cost of £14,000.

[1] Patents 434,225, 7 May 1934 and 463,458, 18 December 1935.

In September 1930 the Paddington wharf and the Sumner Street branch were closed down, and the whole London factory, with its stock and distribution departments, was housed in a modern building reconstructed for the purpose at Wharfedale Road, King's Cross, on the Regent's Canal, and near to King's Cross, St. Pancras and Euston stations. The London offices remained at the Old Bailey.

The provincial branches continued at Belfast, Birmingham, Bristol, Glasgow, Leeds, Liverpool, Manchester, Newcastle and Nottingham. A new stock warehouse was opened at Cardiff in the autumn of 1931, and an Edinburgh office at 42 Frederick Street, in 1935. The Leeds factory (originally one of Millington's) was closed down in June 1939, the work being transferred to Manchester.

Overseas trade was not particularly profitable at this time. In 1927 difficulties over exchange, particularly with India, had to be met by cover from General Reserve. A reduction of dividend in 1930 and 1931 was attributed in large measure to overseas losses. In 1933, however, the firm saw its way to authorize the expenditure of £20,000 for the extension of the Cape Town factory.

A printing-machinery workshop was set up at Calcutta in 1933 at a cost of some £6,000, and an existing factory was purchased in Cairo in 1934, in which year an office—since closed—was opened in Jerusalem.

In Sydney two more floors were built on Croxley House, electric lifts and hoists installed, and the development of printing (especially for envelopes), stationery and labels progressed apace. In 1934 the Sydney factory was further enlarged at a cost of nearly £16,000.

In January 1930 the Board recommended the formation of a separate subsidiary Company for New Zealand. J. W. Randall, the Company's Secretary, visited Australasia in 1931. In 1932 Croxley House, Wellington, was doubled in size, a battery of new machines installed, and the factory left free to operate as a self-contained unit. The Christchurch warehouse was opened, and a Dunedin branch, opened in 1928, was in 1932 moved to better premises on Vogel Street. The Auckland warehouse, after a fire at its original premises, moved to Croxley House, Federal Street.

The export trade with South America had been developed in the years after 1924, but in 1930 and 1931 serious trading losses had to be acknowledged, amounting to nearly £10,000. The department was reorganized on a smaller scale. In 1927 Messrs. Picciotto of New York became the firm's selling agents for stationery in the United States; and in July that year put through the first telephone call the firm had ever received from America.

XVI

THE SECOND WORLD WAR
AND AFTER

1939–1954

THE SECOND WORLD WAR came to a Europe already
half prepared for it. As early as 1936 an Air-Raid Precautions Committee had been formed at Dickinson's with
representatives from each Mill, and by September 1938 A.R.P.
plans were in readiness in all the Mills. At that time gas-mask
assembly work was undertaken by girls both at Apsley and
Tottenham. In the last week of September 1938 the normal
demand for paper dropped heavily, but increased orders were
received from local authorities and His Majesty's Stationery
Office. Overtime was worked for Government orders, especially
for boxes and carriers for gas-masks and for labels and stationery
for the Royal Navy.

The Munich agreement brought hopes of peace; but by
March 1939 the likelihood of war was recognized. Arrangements were made for the quick release of Territorials, and the
expenditure of £20,000 on air-raid shelters at Apsley and
Tottenham was authorized.

On 22 April the President of the Board of Trade formed an
Advisory Committee on the Paper and Board Industry, on
which Mr. Bone, the Manager of Nash Mills, represented
Dickinson's. Mr. Ralph Reed, the Paper Controller designate,
was introduced to the members, and No. 1 Paper Control
Order, regulating prices, communicated to them, so that it
could be brought into action at once when needed.

In June 1939 the firm did what it could to facilitate an appeal for recruits to the Territorial Army. When war was declared on 3 September 210 men left Apsley alone in the first fortnight to join their regiments. Allowances were at once granted to married men with dependents, up to half their normal wages and salaries. A bonus was granted to meet the rise in the cost of living for those who stayed at work. By January 1941 no fewer than 1,500 men were with the forces; a year later 1,894 men and women had joined up. In June 1940 the Apsley Mills section of Local Defence Volunteers (Home Guard) was formed, with another section at the Basildon works.

At the outbreak of war the air-raid precautions already provided for at Apsley and Tottenham were extended to the smaller Mills; at Nash Mills alone they cost £2,000. The provision of black-out in the Mills was difficult, but was duly met, and a fire-watching rota was set up.

The operation of the Paper Control came into force in the first week of the war. On 11 September waste-paper merchants were granted an increase of £1 a ton, plus cost of cartage, but no increase in price was granted to the paper-makers. On 25 October an Order laid down that all paper-makers were to pay a levy of £6 9s. od. a ton on bleached sulphite and £3 12s. od. a ton on mechanical wood and wood pulp in stock or held at any United Kingdom port on their behalf. On wood pulp alone Nash Mills had to pay £7,365. These payments provided a fund which enabled the Paper Control to take over all outstanding contracts, and to distribute pulp to the industry at a fixed price of £17 14s. od. a ton for bleached sulphite and £9. 12s. od. a ton for mechanical wood. The waste-paper merchants were granted a further increase of £1 a ton, and paper-makers were allowed to increase their prices by about 25 per cent. Considering that pulp cost 50 per cent more than before the war, and waste paper about 25 per cent, the trade was not satisfied. The Envelope Makers and Manufacturing Stationers' Association was revived, under the chairmanship of E. G. Parris of Dickinson's, to present the makers' case to the Government. On 24 May 1940 paper producers were allowed 10 per cent more on extras, and an average of £2 more on each ton of paper.

The first official rationing of pulp supplies to the Mills was imposed by a Control of Paper Order issued on 9 February 1940. From 3 March 1940 to 31 May, 60 per cent of the tonnage supplied in the same period in 1939 was received. On 13 April, as a result of the Russian attack on Finland, the ration was cut to 30 per cent, and the Dickinson Mills (notably Nash) had to fall back on waste. On 30 March another heavy charge was imposed on all stocks of wood pulp; Nash Mills alone had to pay £6,800. Selling prices were officially raised by some 11 per cent. In April the invasion of Norway brought the supply of Scandinavian pulp to an end. The situation became worse with the invasion of Holland and Belgium, and the control of paper supplies was tightened.

On 31 May the rationing system was superseded by an allocation by licence. After 2 June it averaged only 40 per cent of the 1939 average, and after September, 35 per cent. At the same time output was compulsorily restricted.[1] By December 1940 supplies of the dextrins and starches used by the papermills and the paper-converting departments were controlled, this time by the Ministry of Food. In March 1941 the quota of supplies of raw materials was fixed at 20 per cent of those received in the same quarter of 1939. A protest by the manufacturers was followed by an increase of 5 per cent in June. In March 1942 further reductions were imposed, ranging from $2\frac{1}{2}$ to 5 per cent; they were again followed by a slight increase in June.

The imposition of Purchase Tax on 21 October 1940 added to the firm's difficulties. There was much trouble over its application, and negotiations with the Treasury continued until

[1] The import of foreign paper was forbidden in November 1940.

February 1941. In May 1941 Captain Crookshank, the Financial Secretary, received a deputation from the trade, on which Dickinson's was represented, on the anomalies it offered, but their representations did not have much success.

Meanwhile Dickinson's was suffering severe losses through direct enemy action. On 19 October 1940 an oil bomb which fell on the Tottenham works caused a fire which completely destroyed the Despatch Department.[1] On 24 October the Birmingham factory was damaged by blast, and four days later more severely by a direct hit by an incendiary bomb. In the same raid the warehouse in Great Charles Street was completely gutted, and the office and show-room in Edmund Street less seriously damaged. In November the firm's premises in Broadmead, Bristol, were totally destroyed with all their contents.[2] In January 1941 the branch office in Redcross Street, Liverpool, was entirely destroyed; temporary accommodation was taken in Paradise Street, which was destroyed in its turn in May of the same year.

On the night of 10–11 May 1941 the offices at 65 Old Bailey, which the firm had occupied since 1809, were totally destroyed by fire, spreading from the Edinburgh Press, after a gallant fight by the fire-watchers. Little or nothing could be saved, and many valuable records were destroyed. On 1 June Croxley House at Manchester was damaged, but here at least the damage was not irremediable.

Meanwhile the shift to war production in the Mills was gathering momentum. In January 1941, when 1,500 employees had joined the Services, it was decided that the firm should undertake as much war-work as possible in order to become a 'protected' establishment doing at least 80 per cent Government

[1] Raids also severely damaged neighbouring residential areas, and fifty homeless workers and their families were temporarily housed at Shendish.

[2] The Bristol branch factory had been closed down in June 1940.

business. The Mills were doing 60 per cent in the Envelope and Manufactured Stationery Departments by the beginning of June, and reached the target in the ensuing quarter. A certificate of protection and essential work was applied for in October, which would give lower age limits for exemption from military service. Two Government inspectors were sent to spend a fortnight in the Mills, in constant conference with the General and Departmental Managers.

'They came', it was said at the time, 'with one clear objective, to extract as many workers as possible from Apsley Mills for transfer to Munition Factories. They were particularly keen to take Engineers from our employ for Shadow Factories. Such had been the development of our own War effort during the year and such was our immediate programme for expansion in the production of accessories for the Ministry of Aircraft Production and the Ministry of Supply, that they finally left without taking a single man or girl from us.

'Instead they went back to recommend that the unique character of the organization they had visited demanded that labour should be supplied to us and local [Labour] Exchanges were instructed to conduct as much labour as possible towards Apsley Mills.'

The certificates were granted and renewed through the war years. By the end of 1941 every Dickinson worker had a civilian steel helmet.

In 1941 the Engineering Department was wholly engaged on Munitions and Ministry of Supply work, and the Card and Pocket Envelope Departments on other Government requirements, chiefly light engineering. By the end of the year the Banker Envelope Department was making shell containers, work which was extended to include night-work. In that year the Household Department was manufacturing cups for Rifle grenade 68 mark 3; glazed board washers; glazed board cups for 2-pounder shells; 2·3-inch L.P. tubes for 3-inch trench mortar bombs; and ammunition carriers for 2-inch grenades. The Label Department was producing tubes for 25-pounder shells; small closing cups for Verey cartridges; closing cups for 6-pounder shells; and paper grummets for protecting driving bands of 2-pound, 6-pound, and 25-pound shells. The Card Department was making T.N.T. demolition cartons; 1¼ lb. 3-inch ammunition carriers (mortar bombs); paper cylinders for gun-cotton primers; delay tubes for 2 inch mortars; and transit discs for 3-inch mortar bombs. The Book Department was producing 2-inch mortar carriers; anti-aircraft millboard washers; and millboard discs for pyrotechnic flares; and the Banker Department was making 3·7 anti-aircraft shell cartridge containers. In July 1942 experiments were made in the Packing Supplies Department in the production of small air craft parts in plastic, and the Pocket Envelope Department changed over to work in plastics from making plugs for aircraft.

Croxley manufactured board for fuse caps, special paper for maps, and the anti-Radar paper which helped to protect bomber crews over enemy targets. Its esparto plant was modified to 'digest' straw at a cost of some £3,000, and the beaters dealt with vast quantities of varied and often unsuitable salvage. In the autumn of 1941 a new Yarrow Boiler, installed there at a cost of over £83,000, came into work, together with a new super-calender 120 inches wide, new rag-breakers and a new machine for cutting and teasing jute. The Croxley Stationery Department was closed down at the end of 1942, and the section for typewriting-papers integrated in the Mill.[1]

The conscription of women between the ages of twenty and thirty in January 1942 seriously affected the supply of workers, especially at Apsley. It was decided that girls leaving to join the forces should be given a fortnight's pay, like single men. At the same time there was a great intake of women to be trained for skilled and semi-skilled engineering. They worked both night- and day-shifts, and proved their worth. At the beginning of

[1] Mr. Macnaughton resigned as Manager at the end of March 1942, and Mr. Bone, from Nash Mills, was appointed to succeed him.

1944 two empty garages were requisitioned at Berkhamsted where some fifty women, who could not be directed far from their homes, worked part-time. By May 1944 one hundred and thirty-two women were working there.

In June 1942 four Labour Inspectors, all experienced engineers, visited Apsley and were much pleased by the complete change-over from peace-time to war-time production. No employees were taken. In September an Essential Work Order was received which covered almost all the departments at Apsley and Tottenham.

In August 1943 Post Office officials approached the firm to ask if envelopes could be made and an airgraph inserted into each on the same machine. The experiment was successful, and by the end of the month 732,000 had been made. By the end of October 1½ million a week were being produced; by Christmas 2 million.

As early as November 1939 the black-out requirements made changes necessary in the hours of work. Saturday morning had to be worked, while the Mills closed earlier on other days. In February 1940 'Summer Time' made it possible to return to a five-day week of forty-five hours. By July 1942 working hours had risen to forty-nine a week. Then, under pressure from the Man Power Board of the Ministry of Labour, they were increased to fifty-two, and for office staff from forty-three to forty-six, with normal overtime payments for extra hours. To meet these requirements the whole of Apsley Mill had to be blacked out, at a cost of £8,800. It was also camouflaged from the air and ground by the firm's own maintenance staff.[1]

In August 1940 a cost-of-living bonus was awarded to workers in the industry by the National Arbitration Tribunal. In March 1941 a further cost-of-living bonus was given to Craft Workers,

[1] A complete public address and radio system was installed at Apsley and Tottenham in February 1943.

ranging from 10s. to 3s. a week. In April the Company extended this to Staff workers who were earning less than £350 a year. In November a further general wage increase was agreed, and wages at the Mills were brought up to the level of those required by the Printing and Kindred Trades Federation.

In September 1941 the temporary workers at Apsley, then numbering over 1,500, were invited to take up Associate Membership of the Union of the House of Dickinson. The payment of the usual subscription admitted them to all benefits but that of pension. The majority joined the House Union.

The institution of P.A.Y.E. in April 1944 involved a change in the pay week. Thereafter it ended on Saturday instead of on Wednesday, with payment made on the following Friday. The firm issued loans on request to cover the week of change, which fell in December.

In November 1939 the issue of Employee's Ordinary stock was stopped in the interests of War Savings. A 'Wings for Victory' campaign in May 1943 resulted in the purchase of £38,529 War Savings Certificates.

The Board began to face the post-war problems as early as February 1943. They then set up committees to consider trading after the war in the various departments, and to draw up plans for any necessary reorganization. In October they decided to offer a rehabilitation grant of £25 to every man discharged from the Forces on medical grounds after not less than twelve months' absence.

By this time, thanks to the Company's heavy contributions towards back service, the Pensions Fund of the Union was no longer dependent on the Company, but had over £1,500,000 invested in Trustee securities. In June 1946 it was agreed that Craft Workers' pensions should be at increased rates, and that pensions should become non-contributory when the proposed comprehensive National Insurance Act became fully operative. At that time the firm's contributions to Union Funds totalled

£1,310,000, with £30,000 for administrative expenses. J. W. Randall, speaking at the meeting that made these decisions, declared:

'When—twenty years ago—we were given the Charter of the Union of the House of Dickinson . . . we were pledged—"To join forces to make the House of Dickinson what a great industry should be—a united family, working with unselfish devotion for the common good, governed by a stewardship that secures for all the just reward of their labour."

'In simple words, we recognized that through our Union we could forge a relationship between Management and Labour where each interest is working for the good of the whole . . .

'In the course of the last twenty years we have seen the benefits, in which all have shared, that have come from the establishment of a spirit of co-operation between us.'

The meeting was the beginning of a campaign for higher production. In July 1946 a Works Committee was formed at Croxley to discuss and advise on matters relating to production and efficiency. The Plastics Department was moved to premises in the Kirkby district of Liverpool, to give space for development at Apsley.[1] In May 1947, when the British Industries Fair was again held at Olympia, Dickinson's had an imposing stand.

In 1945 D. M. Skeins and R. S. Dove retired from managerial work, the former remaining a Director for two years more, and the latter being replaced on the Board by E. G. Parris. J. W. Randall[2] was appointed the sole Managing Director of the Company, at home and overseas. In December 1947 W. E. Ellens retired from the Board, after fifty years with the Company.

---

[1] By March 1949 it was making pens, pencils and other plastic goods; cotton bags (transferred from the Manchester factory), Seal-Easi pocket envelopes (transferred from Apsley) and news-wrappers. The Plastic Department closed down little more than a year later, but the factory now forms a major part of the Packing Division, producing Karrier and Counter bags, laminated metal foil papers and boards, printed and embossed wrappers, and speciality products.

[2] Elected Chairman in 1955.

D. V. Bonsor, the Chairman's younger son, was appointed in his place.[1]

War-time restrictions on supplies and production were gradually lifted. In August 1944 the allocation for personal stationery was at last increased by 10 per cent. In September fire-watching ended, and in October working hours were reduced from fifty-two to forty-nine a week and office hours from forty-six to forty-three. In February 1945 there was another general increase in the allocation.

Raw materials continued in short supply, but by the end of 1946 esparto was coming in more freely. At the beginning of 1947 the allocation reached 66 per cent of the figure for 1939. The wood pulp situation, however, remained extremely difficult; at Croxley further cuts in the Government quota reduced the supply to 139 tons a week. In 1948 the price was raised and the quota reduced to 130 tons, but supplies of esparto went up to pre-war levels, and in the following year paper control at last came to an end.[2]

The Mills were closed for two days' paid holiday when hostilities in Europe ended on 7 May 1945, and again to celebrate victory in the East on 14 August 1945. The normal holiday week was then reinstituted. In October 1945 the first men (other than those released on medical grounds) returned from the Forces, and the Rehabilitation Officer arranged a week's introductory course for them. Others followed at fortnightly intervals. In May 1946 a Day Continuation School was started at Apsley, with F. W. Kellaway, B.SC., as Principal, in co-operation with the Herts County Council, as an interim scheme before the establishment of a County College. It was closed in 1952.

At the Converting Mills a five-day working week of forty-five hours for Craft Workers and forty hours for Staff was

[1] Appointed Managing Director 1955.

[2] In 1949 A. E. Rayner, who had acted as Sales Manager since 1936, became Manager at Croxley. He was in 1955 elected a member of the Board, together with Mr. S. T. Tearle, from the Apsley Mills.

resumed in February 1946. In October of that year a new wages and hours award gave a reduction of one and a half hours a week working time, and a wage increase of 10s. to most men and 7s. 6d. to most women Craft Workers. Apsley Mills and Tottenham then closed at 4.30 on Friday afternoons. In July 1947 all the Mills were for the first time closed for a fortnight for the workers' holiday with pay. A great appeal was made for increased production in 1949 in the national economic crisis. The working week was temporarily increased to forty-five hours, and the ten-minute break periods in morning and afternoon were suspended. An average drop of 10 per cent in selling price on Croxley paper was followed in 1950 by a rise in the cost of raw materials which had to be compensated.

In May 1944 the Company secured temporary City offices on the fourth and fifth floors of a building in New Bridge Street; in October 1948 these were followed by Dickinson House, at 35–8 in the same street,[1] roughly on the site of the ancient Dominican House of Blackfriars.

The Government scheme for creating New Towns found expression in the Town and Country Planning Act of 1947. When the sites for New Towns were designated, Hemel Hempstead proved to be one of them, in spite of its historic antiquity. The original scheme included the compulsory acquisition of the freehold of the land on which Apsley Mills stand. At the inquiry held in December 1946 evidence was given by representatives of Dickinson's as well as by those of other interests adversely affected by the scheme. Ultimately it was decided that the boundaries of the New Town should be adjusted to exclude the Mills.

In January 1945 it was possible once again to make contact with overseas countries. E. G. Kemp, the Factory Manager of the Card Department, H. J. Warrell, the Chief Designer of the Engineering Department, and M. J. Curran, the Chief Chemist

[1] The new offices were opened on 1 October 1949.

at Apsley, went to the United States on behalf of the Ministry of Supply to study production methods for packing materials providing protection against tropical climates and rough handling on improvised landing-beaches. In August 1945 E. O. Rance, F. J. Delderfield and R. W. Westrope visited America to regain contact with the firm's agents. In August 1946 E. G. Parris went to the United States for two months to renew the firm's American contacts.

In the winter of 1946–7 the whole country experienced the rigours of a crisis in coal production. By the end of January 1947 the stock at Apsley was at danger point. A notice had to be issued that the Mills would close down on 14 February unless there were an increase in coal supplies. No more coal came in, and the Mills had to shut. Unemployment Benefit was paid through the firm's own wages officers. At Apsley 'After a week's experience of Shut Down under winter conditions, it was found that the amount of steam necessary to heat the Mills generated enough power for lighting, pumps, lifts and other essential services. We satisfied ourselves that if we started up the oil-engine it would give us power adequate to run most of the machines in our Engineering Shop, and after consultation ... our Engineers were recalled to work on February 24th on the clear understanding that they came back on a week to week basis. On Friday, March 7th, after three weeks' shut, we were able to inform our workers that supplies of coal had been delivered that would enable Apsley Mills to reopen on Monday, March 10th for four days, and subsequently a notice was posted to the effect that the prevailing weather conditions, coupled with slightly improved coal deliveries, would enable us to resume working a 5 day week immediately.'

Conditions were worse at Tottenham, which depended on external power. There, the management 'met our Workers on Monday morning at 8 o'clock (10 February) in a cold and silent factory. We explained the position and told them they would be paid in accordance with the Trade Agreement.' There, too, there was a gradual return to normal conditions, and by 3 March the factory was again at work.

In October 1948 a new Sports Pavilion was opened at Shendish, the gift of Mr. and Mrs. Boyd Thompson in memory of their son Captain Richard Boyd Thompson, Royal Buckinghamshire Yeomanry, killed on active service in Burma in 1944 —formerly a keen member of the Guild of Sport.

There has everywhere been ceaseless activity and constant building and rebuilding. At Kirkby, Liverpool, extensive buildings have been set up on a site as large as the whole of that which Apsley occupies.

In the years immediately following the war the overseas branches had been continuing their work more or less independently. The Australian branch had been able to install a waxing plant in the Melbourne factory, and greatly improved envelope and card machinery in the Sydney factory. The policy for overseas development has been gradually clarified. Now, whenever a manufacturing unit for the production of the Dickinson range of stationery can be profitably developed, the local manager is encouraged to set it up. If a machine can be kept fully employed at the point of consumption it is readily made available. As a consequence Dickinson factories are operating in Cairo, Johannesburg, Durban, Cape Town, Sydney and Wellington. The modern factory at Hamilton, Ontario, is run by the recently inaugurated firm of John Dickinson & Co. (Canada) Ltd. The parent firm now has branches in India at Calcutta, Bombay and Madras; in Pakistan at Karachi; in Burma at Rangoon; in Ceylon at Colombo; in the Far East at Singapore; in the Near East at Cairo, Alexandria and Cyprus; in Africa at Cape Town, Johannesburg, Durban, East London, Port Elizabeth, Pretoria, Bloemfontein, Salisbury, Bulawayo and Nairobi; in Australia at Sydney, Melbourne, Brisbane and Adelaide; in New Zealand at Wellington, Auckland, Christchurch and Dunedin; in Canada at Hamilton, Ontario. There is a branch in Dublin, and offices and local service stock-rooms in Belfast, Birmingham, Bristol, Cardiff, Glasgow, Leeds, Liverpool, and Manchester with a London Depot at King's Cross. Further offices are maintained in Edinburgh, Exeter, Newcastle upon Tyne and Nottingham.

In 1953 a new issue of £2,900,000 Ordinary stock was authorized, on a basis of one for one, making a total Equity issue of £5,800,000.

The Twenty-Eighth Annual General Meeting of the Union of the House of Dickinson was held in the Apsley Guildhouse on 24 June 1954. All kinds of grants were reported, for sickness,[1] convalescence, unemployment; grants made to relatives on death before retirement, and others given on various compassionate grounds from an accumulated General Benefit Fund totalling £27,972.[2] Pension payments amounted to £93,620 to 668 pensioners. It was reported that since the foundation of the Union in 1926 the Company's contributions to its funds had totalled £2,470,000. In the current financial year the Union's share of the Company's profits had been a fifth of the £1,500,000 earned. The Union's income from investments amounted to £169,000, of which more than half came from John Dickinson stock, in which it is by far the largest shareholder.[3]

The report serves to show how far the Union of the House of Dickinson has succeeded. Its basis has always been the belief that there are not two sides in the Dickinson Company, but that the interests of everyone, without exception, are bound up in the continuing progress and prosperity of the firm. Ling's belief in the idea of a Union, united under its Charter to be the expression of the House of Dickinson as a united family, is embodied in the Union as it is today. Its moral force has brought

[1] Over 2,500 claims for sickness were paid during the year.
[2] This includes the J. E. Hunt Benevolent Fund.
[3] The Union holds 40 per cent of the Debenture, 25 per cent of the Preference, and 13 per cent of the Ordinary stock.

together all its members—Directors, Managers, Staff and Craft Workers—in a bond of fellowship and mutual trust. All employees are now free to decide for themselves whether or not they wish to belong to their appropriate Trade Union; but the basic principles, spiritual and material, of Ling's creation still stand.

It is a hundred and fifty years since John Dickinson set up in business; a hundred and forty-five years since he invented his paper-making machine and set up his Mill at Apsley; a hundred and thirty-seven years since he patented a process for making duplex paper and for machine-sizing; a hundred and thirty-three years since he experimented in paste for cardboard on the kitchen stove at Nash Mills, and 'had his dinner baked in consequence'; a hundred and four years since he first had an envelope cut and folded by machinery in his Mill.

Much has been sacrificed to the making of the business besides the capital that John Dickinson got together: much of his own potential scientific knowledge, something of his own humanity; his wife's hopes of domestic happiness; his children's love for their father; John Evans's chances of an academic career; the health of R. H. Ling and F. G. Hawdon and many another; the leisure and the interests of generations of engineers and craftsmen and clerks; the comfort of women hurrying across the moor in the cold winter mist or crowding into buses: all these have been given up to the devouring Mills. In the East they believe that no building stands secure unless its foundations have been strengthened by human sacrifice; and into the foundations of the House of Dickinson has gone the tribute of many lives.

Could John Dickinson return to the valley of which he began to deface the beauty and to create the prosperity, he would still find landmarks that he knew: much of the Cottage at Apsley Mills; the house, the bridge and part of the Canal at Nash; his old Salle at Croxley; and a few walls at Home Park. His house of Abbot's Hill still exists as a girls' school; his partner's house at Shendish, as the sports club of his firm; of the friends' and relations' houses he used to visit, many survive, if turned to institutional uses. The church at Leverstock Green that he helped to build (himself no church-goer) still serves its parish; the almshouses for which he gave the land still serve the needs of retired stationers; the school he built in Nash Mills village still stands, if empty.

He would find that in the sprawling and productive world that bore his name he was still a legend. In his valley men have not wholly forgotten the stories of his quick wits, his angry haste, his rough justice and his mechanical skill. What would please him best would be to find that though none of his descendants was left to bear his patronymic, the name of John Dickinson still stood for business honesty and good paper, and that the firm that bore it still follows his principles of manufacture, maintaining through the generations a pride in the Dickinson tradition of hard work, fine craftsmanship, and service to all the interests with which it is privileged to be associated.

APPENDICES

Note Book of P. Meadows Taylor, 1823

MEN AT APSLEY MILLS

John Durrant, Engineer
Wm. Putman, Assist.
Thos. Chuter, Engineer
Jas. Smith, Assist.
Morris Chuter. Junr., Picker
Thos. Perry, Pressman Dust Rags and Carrier of $\frac{1}{2}$ Stuff

Thos. Lane, Engineer ⎫
George Skurrinel, Do. ⎬ Steam Engines and Washers
Thos. Green, Assistant ⎭

James Collins ⎫
Thos. Jennings ⎪
M. Smith ⎬ Steam Engine Men
Hy. Hunt ⎭

MACHINE HOUSE

James Francis   Gt. machine
John Francis   2 small machines
Joseph Freeman ⎫
Wm. Ridgeway ⎬ Cutters
Philip Rending,   Steam Rolls
Joseph Gate,   do.   Assist.

DRY WORKERS

John Owen
Dean, old man
Wm. Harvey, sub. Hostler Bill
Hy. Howard, short man
James Latham, thin man
Thos. Collins, Boy
Jerem^{a} Rose ⎫
Wm. Andrews ⎬ Pressers

SALLE

Henry Barton

John Hippitt, Finisher

Abm. Hunt, do.

Thos. Davies, do.

Henry Boddington, do.

John Chapman, do.

Francis Patrick

George Hill ⎫
Thos. Perry ⎬ Pressers

Josiah Freeman, cutter of dry paper

MILLWRIGHT

John Howze

James Martin

NASH MILL

John Hutchinson ⎫
John Smith ⎬ Pressers

James Mutton ⎫ Dryworker
Wm. Philips ⎬ do. & sizing
Child ⎬
Francis ⎭ do.

Sparks, Finisher

Peacock ⎫
Tims ⎬ do.

Benjn. Francis

Lawrence, Cutter of Dry Paper

CARPENTERS

Saunders

Goss

Britney

A. Marshall, Foreman

CARPENTERS—*continued*

Joseph Lloyd
Joseph Lane
Henry Kempster } Engineers
Thomas Rhodes

Richd. Rhodes
              Parrot } Assists.

Chas. Green
B. Norris } do.

N.M. MACHINES

James Gamblin
Thos. Latchford
Henry Howe
John Stevens } Assist. do.
Ringshall—Steam Rolls
Catlin—Assist. do.
Thos. Freeman
              Clarke } Cutters

Croxley Mill in the Eighteen Seventies

by W. A. Stephenson, 1939

Below is a list of names of those working in the Mill in the seventies.

SALLE

Old John Raggett (Foreman)
Albert Raggett
John Raggett
William Raggett
Charles Cheater
Tom Warn
John Chapman

SHEETERS

Mrs. Bunker
Mrs. A. Raggett
Mrs. J. Raggett
Mrs. W. Raggett
Mrs. C. Cheater
Mrs. Slaughter
Mrs. Pudd
Maria Raggett
Sarah Toms
Sarah Kempster

CUTTING MACHINE ROOM

George Gamble
Harry East
Six Boys

MACHINE HOUSE
No. 1 Machine (shake)—only run on special orders
No. 2 Machine William Gantang?
              James Groom
No. 3 Machine William Kempster
              Joe Kempster
No. 4 Machine John Foster
              William Sear
} on 24 hour shifts

BEATER HOUSE
Beater Men
Richard Saunders
John Brown
Tom King
David King
James Holliman
David Kempster
Helpers
Joe Foster
Charles Sears
James Webb
Tom Southam
} on 24 hour shifts
Stuff Pickers (from the Beaters)
Eight Boys on 12 hour shifts

PAPER SOAKING HOUSE
John Toppin
Edward Gibson
George Toms

HALF STUFF (LITTLE MILL)
Joe Bunker
Stephen Saunders } on 24 hour shifts
Four young men
Two boys

TOP SALLE (SHAVING SORTING)
Walter Rance (Foreman)
Jerry Saunders
Four young men
Four boys
Twelve young women and girls

ENGINE & BOILER MEN
Tom Hobbs
Tom Chilton

MILLWRIGHT
Isaac Winter

CARPENTER
William Went

GENERAL LABOURERS
William Mead ⎫ About half time on
Richard Pudd ⎭ River work
William West
Tom Holt
John Slaughter
William Clark

POST BOY
To Nash Mills (Head Office)
Daily walk (via the Parks)

(Signed) W. A Stephenson

Apsley Mill April 9, 1881

PERSONS EMPLOYED IN PAPER DEPARTMENT

	No. of Men	No. of Boys	No. of Women	No. of Girls	Total
Half Stuff Dusters . .	3				3
Half Stuff Overlookers .	2	12	2		16
Helpers. . . .	4				4
Engineers . . .	4				4
Engine Boys. Pickers .		4			4
Paper Soakers . .	2	1			3
Machines. Paper . .	13	4			17
Millers	4	14		11	29
Finishers . . .	4		13		17
Engine Drivers . .	5				5
Fireman . . .	1				1
Gasman . . .	1				1
Size Maker . . .	1				1
Carpenters . . .	3				3
Millwright . . .	1				1
Gas Fitter . . .	1				1
Laborers . . .	5				5
Storekeeper & Assistant .	1	1			2
Manager . . .	1				1
	56	36	15	11	118

PERSONS EMPLOYED IN CARD DEPARTMENT

	No. of Men	No. of Boys	No. of Women	No. of Girls	Total
Pasting	13	18	1		32
Pressing . . .	5				5
Hanging . . .	4				4
Paste Boiling . . .	1	1			2
Milling	1	4			5
Rolling	1	1		1	3
Cutting . . .	9	1			10
Overlooking . . .			9		9
Counting . . .			5	3	8
Packing . . .	1	1			2
Finishing . . .	1	1			2
Laying Facings . .			5		5
Boxmaking . . .		1	1	1	3
Foreman & Assistant .	2				2
	38	28	21	5	92

PERSONS EMPLOYED IN ENVELOPE DEPARTMENT

	No. of Men	No. of Boys	No. of Women	No. of Girls	Total
Punchers . . .	5	5			10
Gummers . . .	10	2	2	30	44
B. Borderers . . .			71		71
F. P. Stampers . .	7	1	1		9
Envelope Folders . .	9	7		31	47
Envelope Overlookers .			47		47
Official Folders . .	2		17	5	24
Envelope Packers . .	2				2
Envelope Sorters. broken.	2				2
Fitters	4				4
Foreman . . .	1				1
	42	15	138	66	261

TOTAL NUMBER EMPLOYED

	No. of Men	No. of Boys	No. of Women	No. of Girls	Total
Paper Department . .	56	36	15	11	118
Card Department . .	38	28	21	5	92
Envelope Department .	42	15	138	66	261
	136	79	174	82	471

Men .	136
Boys .	79
Women .	174
Girls .	82
471	Total

Nash Mills

SALLE FINISHERS: 6 MEN
W. Peacock, J. Davis, S. Harcourt, F. Atkins, H. Lane,
J. Sawyer (Jogger)

SALLE WOMEN: 19
Mrs. Coleman, Mrs. Hill, J. Groome, Mrs. Porter, Mrs. Smith,
A. Atkins, Mrs. Tyers, Mrs. Barnes, R. Lane, E. Mutton,
Mrs. Smith, Mrs. Jeffery, J. Garner, C. Pope, Mrs. Ricket,
M. Bristow, E. Smith, Mrs. Draper, A. Morris

ENGINE HOUSE (PICKERS): 4 WOMEN, 3 GIRLS, 1 MAN
J. Hoar, Mrs. Porter, M. Finch, E. Edmunds,
Mrs. Birchmore, Mrs. Hall, Mrs. Atkins, G. Sells

ENGINE MEN: 6 MEN
W. Ricket, H. Coleman, G. Tibbles, E. Coker, H. Morris,
J. Cashmore

HELPERS: 5 MEN
J. Mutton, W. Lane, J. Smith, G. Hill, J. Hill

ESPARTO BREAKING: 1 MAN, 1 BOY
A. Cripps, F. Quick

BLEACHERS: 2 MEN
F. Plummer, E. Sells

DUSTERS: 2 MEN, 1 BOY
F. Crawley, J. Timberlake, W. Holliday

PAPER SOAKERS: 2 MEN
J. Birchmore, A. Sexton

APPENDIX C

MACHINE MEN: 3 MEN

F. Freemen, J. Coleman, J. Saunders

MACHINE MENS HELPERS: 3 MEN

W. Smith, T. Lane, A. Freeman

CUTTERS IN MACHINE HOUSE: 1 MAN, 7 BOYS

J. Wilkinson, J. Lane, C. Mutton, L. Holliday, J. Lea, A. North,
W. Tarbox, T. Edmonds

LABOURER: 1 MAN

W. Holmes

FELT SEWER: 1 WOMAN

Mrs. Whittaker

33 Men
24 Women
3 Girls
9 Boys
—
69 Total

Findlay	Fitters	Mims	Fitters
Fleetwood		Harrison	
Allsop		Clarke	
Bulcraig		Saunders	
Winter		Lloyd	
Wright		East	
Harrison		Allsop	
Overhead		Tyers	
Slaughter			
Pettit		North	Fitter's Labourers
Giddens		Blois	

Rhodes	Fitter's Labourers	Holliman	Blacksmiths
Janes		Protheroe	
Mutton		Edmunds	
Lane		Sherfield	
Higby		Rhodes	
Foster		Winfield	
Coker		Crisp	
Fleetwood	Fitter's	Coker	Blacksmith's
Arnold	Apprentices	Wheeler	Strikers
Allsop		Wilson	
Clifton		Freeman	
Freeman		Hunt	
Platt		North	
		Lovett	
Clarke	Grinder		
Manton	Gas Fitters	Mayo	Tin Workers
Atkins		Gurney	
Dearman		Allsop	Tin Worker's
Turner			Apprentice
North			
Gravestock		Rickett	Leather Dept.
Kingham		Young	Leather Dept.
Cromack			Apprentice
Janes	Oilman	Clarke	Wire Weavers
		Weightman	
Coleman	Errand Boy		
		Atkins	Wire Weaver's
Coker	Time Keeper	Beck	Assistants
Clarke	Clerk	Latchford	Engine Drivers
		Sexton	
Stephenson	Foreman		
		Munn	Stokers
Stephenson	Managing	Puddifoot	
	Engineer		

Mayo	Carpenter's Foreman	Odell Palmer	Plumber's Labourers
		Perry	
Streets	Carpenters	Rhodes	
Clarke		Latchford	
Holliday			
Mayo		Sewell	Journeyman Painter
Mayo			
Barnes			
Searle		Coleman	Plumber's Apprentice
Turner			
Mutton			
Durrant		Clifton	Bricklayers
Bedford		Crawley	
Mayo		Collins	
Durrant		Hoar	
		Chennells	
Cheater	Carpenter's Labourers	Crawley	
Syster			
Mayo	Carpenter's Apprentices	Bovingdon	Bricklayer's Labourers
Mayo		Jeffs	
Kingham		Puddifoot	
		Woodard	
Dowse	Cooper	Plummer	
		Tripp	
Kingham	Sawyers	Tims	
Timberlake		Room	
Coleman		Walker	
		Munn	
Lee	Under Sawyers	Sear	
Rhodes		Coleman	
Gravestock			
Puddifoot	Plumbers	Clifton	Bricklayer's Apprentices
Holloway		Crawley	

243

	No.		*No.*
Fitters . . .	19	Stokers . . .	2
Fitters (Labourers) .	9	Carpenters . . .	13
Fitters (Apprentices) .	6	Carpenters (Labourers)	2
Grinder (At Grindstone)	1	Carpenters (Apprentices)	3
Gas Fitters . . .	8	Carpenter (Foreman) .	1
Oilman . . .	1	Cooper . . .	1
Errand Boy . .	1	Sawyers . . .	3
Time Keeper . .	1	Under Sawyers . .	3
Clerk . . .	1	Plumber (Foreman) .	1
Foreman . . .	1	Plumbers (Labourers) .	5
Blacksmiths . .	7	Plumber (Apprentice) .	1
Blacksmith's Strikers .	7	Plumbers (Journeymen)	2
Tin Workers . .	2	Bricklayer (Foreman) .	1
Tin Worker (Apprentice)	1	Bricklayers . .	5
Leather Dept. . .	1	Bricklayers (Labourers)	12
Leather Dept. (Apprentice)	1	Bricklayers (Apprentices)	2
Wire Weavers . .	2	Managing Engineer .	1
Wire Weavers (Assistants)	2		
Engine Drivers . .	2	Total	131

Croxley Mill, 1881

FINISHERS ETC.: 6 MEN
C. Raggett, T. Warn, J. Raggett, J. Chapman, W. Raggett,
C. Cheater

JOGGERS: 1 MAN
A. Raggett

SHEETERS: 17 WOMEN
A. Cheater, E. Taylor, M. A. Raggett, M. A. Webb, S. Jones,
A. M. Robins, C. Puddifoot, M. A. Raggett, L. Puddifoot,
J. Rance, M. A. Cheater, F. Puddifoot, M. Raggett,
M. Slaughter, S. Toms, N. Bunker, M. Gamblin

CUTTING ROOM DEPT.: 1 MAN, 8 BOYS
G. Gamblin, G. Chapman, W. Carter, H. Gilbert, J. Grover,
W. Croft, W. Raggett, C. Wilson, T. Wellings

PAPER SOAKING DEPT.: 1 MAN, 3 YOUNG MEN, 6 BOYS
J. Toppin, C. Gurney, L. Gibson, A. Turner, W. Hall, F. Clark,
G. Sigrove, A. Evans, E. Kempster, W. Paine

NEW MILL DEPT

HALF STUFF, BLEACHING, ETC.: 2 MEN, 4 BOYS
S. Sanders, D. King, T. Southam, G. J. Cheater, J. Doggett,
B. Robinett

STUFF ENGINE DEPT.: 6 ENGINE MEN
B. Brown, R. Sanders, T. Williams, D. Kempster, J. Cole,
J. Hollaman

6 ENGINE MEN (HELPERS)
J. Foster, C. Sears, M. Hull, J. Webb, B. Payne, E. Toms

ENGINE PICKERS: I MAN, II BOYS
E. West, W. Coster, F. East, G. Groom, J. Wilson, W. Doggett,
T. Rawrence, G. Cooke, F. Atkins, T. Gilby, R. Moor, J. Harris

MACHINE HOUSE: 3 MACHINE MEN
William Sears, William Gravney, William Kempster

3 MACHINE MEN (HELPERS)
James Groom, Joseph Kempster, W. Gibson

BOILER HOUSE: 4 MEN
T. Hobbs, W. Mead, T. Chilton, J. Pudd

MILL WRIGHTS & CARPENTERS: 3 MEN
I. Winter, W. Went, A. Went

LABOURERS: 3 MEN, I BOY
I. Chapman, W. Grover, W. Kempster, H. Gurney

DRY SHAVING DEPT.: 2 MEN
W. Rance, J. Tandy

OVERLOOKERS: 6 WOMEN
M. Norman, C. Puddifoot, M. A. Golding, R. Sills,
M. A. Rackliff, C. Element

SORTERS: I2 WOMEN
M. Hull, E. Powell, S. Haylock, A. Cake, J. Bleacher, E.
Grover, P. Blackwell, M. Moody, M. A. Chapman, M. Hull,
M. Tibbles, A. Foster

11 GIRLS

I. Sills, A. Chapman, A. Holt, M. A. Hollaman, F. Tandy,
J. Haylock, L. Hull, E. Owen, F. Sears, E. Waller, J. Sears

9 BOYS

W. H. Puddifoot, J. Paddick, J. Humphrey, G. W. Groom,
W. Henly, R. Groom, H. Rutland, J. Batten, G. Lawrence

WILLOW & BAG FILLERS: 8 BOYS

H. Brown, H. Wallace, I. Weston, A. Raggett, W. Cripps,
H. Holt, F. Rossin, W. George

F. Haines-Wood
A. Stephenson

BUILDING STAFF, CROXLEY

3 Carpenters
6 Bricklayers
1 Fitter
1 Painter
1 Boy
21 Labourers
—
33 (32 Men and 1 Boy)

SALLE: 5 MEN

S. Saunders, G. Hill, F. Harris, W. Dyer, J. Tyers

BOTTOM SALLE: 10 WOMEN, 1 MAN

Miss Price, Mrs. Morton, Mrs. E. Foster, Mrs. Sturman, Mrs.
Collins, Mrs. Lane, Mrs. Foster, Mrs. Jackson, Miss Brown,
Mrs. Griffin, E. Hill (Jogger)

APPENDIX C

ENGINE MEN: 8 MEN
E. Lunnon, T. Grace, W. White, R. Freeman, J. Dorrofield,
J. Slade, F. Slade, J. Sturman

HELPERS: 4 MEN
G. Rickett, J. Scott, A. Cooper, W. Morris

MACHINE MEN: 3 MEN
W. Kingham, H. Kingham, W. Lane

HELPERS: 3 MEN
H. Hill, H. Austin, T. Wilkinson

CUTTERS IN MACHINE HOUSE: 1 MAN, 8 BOYS
J. Freeman, J. Ridgway, T. Burgin, A. Freeman, J. Freeman,
J. Kemp, L. Crawley, F. Kemp, B. White

BLEACHER: 1 MAN
E. Hill

DUSTERS: 1 MAN, 3 BOYS
G. White, J. Jackson, J. Sells, W. Crawley

ENGINE PICKERS: 1 WOMAN, 3 GIRLS
E. Timberlake, E. Hill, Mrs. Seabrook, E. Foster

COTTON SORTING: 1 MAN, 1 WOMAN, 1 GIRL
G. Dyer, Mrs. Dimmock, A. Attwood

PAPER SORTING: 2 MEN, 3 BOYS
R. How, H. North, A. Hill, G. Biggerstaff, A. Porter

SOAKING PAPER: 1 MAN, 2 BOYS
T. Stokes, W. Burrage, I. Foster

248

APPENDIX C

BOILER MEN, STOKERS: 2 MEN
W. Dimmock, W. Cox

ENGINE TENDERS: 2 MEN
J. Collins, J. Baldwin

MILLWRIGHT
J. Harrison

CARPENTER
A. Scott

LABOURERS: 3 MEN
W. Harding, J. Morton, C. Ridgway

OFFICE: I MAN
A. Hudson

Men	41
Women	12
Boys	16
Girls	4
Total	73

Home Park Mills, April 1881

PAPER STAINING

	Men	Women	Boys	Total	
Colorers		30		30	(20 of these are enamellers)
Color Makers	1		1	2	
Color mixer	1			1	
Size maker	1			1	
Brushers	2			2	
Varnishers	2			2	
Embossers	1		1	2	
Millers	1		5	6	
Sheeters		4		4	
Finisher	1			1	
Env. Band Cutter	1			1	
	11	34	7	52	

Batchworth Mill, April 1881

Return of No. of Employees at above Week Ending April 7th

	Men	Boys	Women	Girls
Cutting and Sorting .			94	3
Overlooking . .			20	
Dusting . . .	2		7	
Devilling . . .	3	11		
Boilers . . .	2			
Potmen . . .	2			
Bleaching . . .	2			
Tub filling . .	4			
Rope Chopping .	1			
Engine Tenders .	4			
Pressers . . .	2			
General Repairs .	6			
Stables . . .	1			
Weighing . . .	1			
Men .	30	11	121	3
Boys .	11			
Women	121			
Girls .	3			
	165			

Frogmore Mill

Names of the people employed at Frogmore Mill, April 1881

Males:		*Occupation:*	
	Walker, A.		Steep House
	Latchford, J.		Do.
	Bass, J.		Stoker
	Wheeler, J.		Do.
	Parish, W.		Evaporator
	Gilmer, T.		Do.
	Brinklow, W.		Do.
	Harrowell, A.		Do.
	Morris, R.		Caustic Breaking
	Puddefoot, D.		Boiling
	Humphrey, H.		Do.
	Wood, D.		Carter
	Hearne, J.		Breaker
	Bass, W.		Do.
	Walker, F.		Helper
	Tomlin, H.		Do.
	Kitchiner, J.		Grass Lifting
17+1	Hoggens, H. (Boy)		Do.

Females:		*Occupation:*	
	Munn, L.		Dusting
	Sexton, S.		Helper
	Sexton, F.		Do.
	Durrant, H.		Weigher
	King, H.		Sorting
	Woodward, E.		Do.
	Moore, E.		Do.
	Hoar, S.		Do.
	Banfield, A.		Do.
	Young, A.		Engine Picker
	Howard, S.		Do.
12	Hemmings, A.		Do.

Two Waters Mill

Names of the people employed at Two Waters Mill, April 1881

Males:	*Occupation:*
Winter, C.	Mechanic
Bedford, G.	Carpenter
Kiff, J.	Smith
Peek, J.	Machine Man
Stratton, H.	Do.
Crawley, H.	Dryer
Waller, J.	Do.
Puddefoot, J.	Engineer
Slade, J.	Do.
Baldwin, J.	Helper
Tibbles, A.	Do.
Bass, C.	Do.
Mallard, W.	Do.
Brinklow, D.	Carter
Wiseman, S.	Stoker
Chater, W.	Do.
Howse, R.	Odd Man
Picton, A.	Do.
Howse, C.	Finisher
Shirley, W.	Do.
Warrall, W. (Boy)	Do.
Collins, W.	Paper Lifter
Street, J. (Boy)	Machine Boy
Sear, J.	Cutting Machine
Spicer, T.	Clay Mixing
Pratt, W. (Boy)	Do.
Janes, M.	
Gisborne, T. J.	Clerk
Warrall, J.	Foreman
27+3 Hayes, G. W.	

Females:		*Occupation:*	
	Pipkin, S.	Rag Sorter
	Beckley, S.	Do.
	Warby, S.	Do.
	Kilby, A.	Do.
	Slade, A. (Girl)	Paper Sorter
	West, E.	Do.
	Peek, E.	Do.
	Slade, R.	Do.
	Morris, S.	Do.
	Mason, M.	Do.
	Puddefoot, E.	Do.
	Puddefoot, A.	Do.
	Picton, M.	Do.
	Preston, A.	Do.
	Crawley, S.	Do.
	Banfield, E.	Do.
	Clarke, H.	Do.
	Kempster, E.	Do.
	Rowe, A.	Do.
	Wharton, A.	Do.
	Blacknell, A.	Cutting Machine
20+2	Turner, M. (Girl)	Do.

COUNTING HOUSE

Mr. Rothney
Mr. E. Carter
Mr. Bristow
Mr. Nichols
Mr. Smith
Mr. Wardley
Mr. Hunt

Mr. Webb
Mr. Payne
Mr. Chasteney

PAPER DEPARTMENT

Mr. Varty
A. Gamblin
C. Martin

PAPER DEPT. (*continued*)

W. French
L. Hall
H. Adams
J. Wilson
W. Dunn (under 18)
C. E. Griffiths
W. Williams
T. Leveritt (Carman)
— Foster (Carman)

CARD DEPARTMENT

Mr. F. Carter
Mr. Ling (under 18)
J. A. Soanes (under 18)
J. E. Blick (under 18)

ENVELOPE DEPARTMENT

Mr. R. Martin
Mr. Cheffins
Mr. Golding
W. Wiles
J. Adams
W. Willing
F. Willing
A. Simpson
G. Morley
C. Gamblin

32+4

List of Staff at Paddington
11th April 1881

NAME	AGE	OCCUPATION
Alfred Cole	36	Assistant
Jas. Bevis	34	Carman
Isaac West	39	Do.
Jas. Foster (O.B.)	33	Do.
Henry Cheeseman	38	Do. & Horsekeeper
John Green	32	Leading Porter
Edward Mawby	51	Porter
William Bardell	46	Do.
William Sells	27	Do.
J. H. Cole	62	Manager

INDEX

Abbeville, 116
Abbot's Hill, 58–69, 88, 101, 174(*n.*), 228
Aberdeen, 57
Adams, H., 255
   J., 255
Africa, firm's post-war branches in, 225 (*see also* South Africa)
Alderson, E. H. 42
Alexandria, branch at, 225
Allsop, —, 241, 242
Ancient Bronze Implements, etc., of Great Britain, 116
Ancient Stone Implements, etc., of Great Britain, 116
Andrews, William, 36, 231
Anthropological Institute, 117
Antiquaries, Society of, 115–17, 134, 166(*n.*)
Anti-Slavery Society, 68
Applegarth, Joseph, 41(*n.*)
Apsley Mill, 15–29, 33, 36, 40, 95, 115, 127–9, 145, 147, 168–73, 187, 198, 204–5, 223, 227
   acquired by J. Dickinson, 12–14
   arson at, 169
   brass band, 156
   cannon at, 96
   closed down, 200, 224
   continuation school, 222
   employees, names of, 231–3
      numbers of, 30, 123, 136, 172, 237–9
   envelope dept., 12(*n.*), 69(*n.*), 122, 127–8, 135, 152–4, 156, 171–3, 191, 204, 206–7, 210, 217, 239

extensions and improvements, 45, 53, 96, 127–9, 152–3, 156–7, 163, 171–2, 191–2, 206–7
fire brigade, 118, 137(*n.*), 152, 191(*n.*), 192–3
gas-works, 126, 135
Guildhouse, 191, 207, 226
in general strike, 199, 200
insurance on (1854), 96(*n.*)
in wartime, 179–80, 213–14, 217–20
printing introduced at, 172
training centre, 191
Apsley, St. Mary's Church, 126
   War Memorial at, 179
Arnold, —, 242
Athenæum, The, 76
Atkins, —, 242
   A., 240
   F., 240, 246
   Mrs., 240
Attwood, A., 248
Austin, H., 248
Australia, firm's branches in, 148, 162, 165, 183, 195–6, 211, 225

Bagster, Samuel, 20, 68, 138
Baldwin, J., 249, 253
Ballantyne & Co., 48, 49
Banfield, A., 252
   E., 254
Bardell, William, 256
Barlow, *see* Pratt Barlow
Barnes, —, 243
   Mrs., 240
Barrs, Edward, 176
Barton, Henry, 232

3. A SECTION OF A MAP OF LONDON IN 1835 SHOWING:
(A) Ludgate Street; (B) Walbrook; (C) 65 Old Bailey; (D) Upper Thames Street; (E) New Bridge Street

5. WORKMEN'S COTTAGES BUILT BY JOHN DICKINSON
Home Park, 1825

6. NO. 3 (DICKINSON CYLINDER) MACHINE AT CROXLEY MILLS

Installed in 1830, dismantled in 1936

7. *above:* NASH MILLS (*c.* 1838) 8. *below:* APSLEY MILLS (*c.* 1838)
both by Harriet Dickinson

9. ABBOT'S HILL
built by John Dickinson in 1836

10. DICKINSON ESSAY LETTERSHEET, 1839

II. NASH MILLS, 1859

12. JOHN DICKINSON (*c.* 1860)

from a photograph

13. JOHN EVANS (c. 1865)

14. PLUMBERS AND PAINTERS AT APSLEY MILLS (*c.* 1865)

15. COLOURING DEPARTMENT, HOME PARK MILLS (c. 1865)

16. ENGINEERS, MILLWRIGHTS AND CARPENTERS, NASH MILLS (c. 1870)

17. ENGINEERS AND MILLWRIGHTS, NASH MILLS, 1874

CROXLEY MILLS
18. *above:* 1872–3   19. *below:* 1929

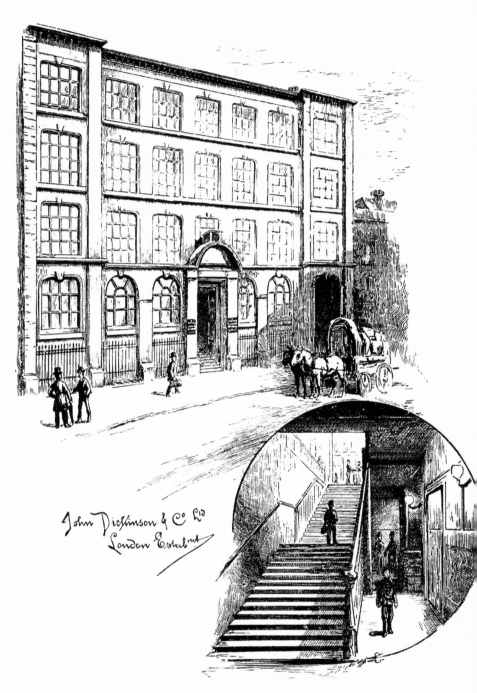

John Dickinson & Co Ltd
London Establisht

20. 65 OLD BAILEY, 1887

21. FREDERICK PRATT BARLOW

22. FRANK PRATT BARLOW

23. G. A. JAMES ROTHNEY (*c.* 1895)

24. THE FIRST PAPER TABLE-NAPKIN

Used in 1887 at the annual dinner of John Dickinson & Co. Ltd.

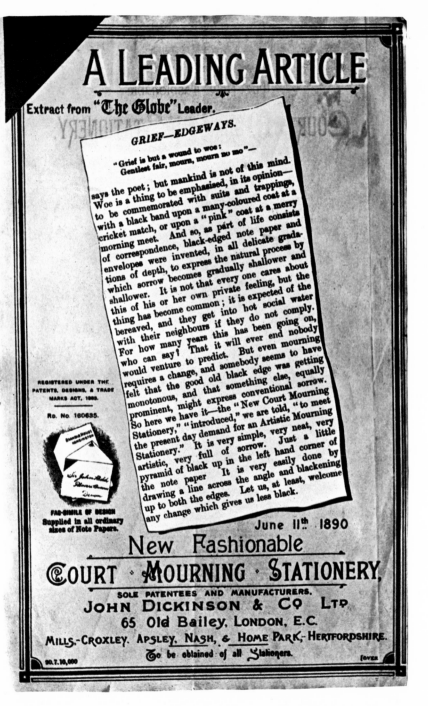

A LEADING ARTICLE

Extract from "The Globe" Leader.

GRIEF—EDGEWAYS.

"Grief is but a wound to woe :
Gentlest fair, mourn, mourn no mo"—

says the poet ; but mankind is not of this mind. Woe is a thing to be emphasised, in its opinion— to be commemorated with suits and trappings, with a black band upon a many-coloured coat at a cricket match, or upon a "pink" coat at a merry morning meet. And so, as part of life consists of correspondence, black-edged note paper and envelopes were invented, in all delicate grada- tions of depth, to express the natural process by which sorrow becomes gradually shallower and shallower. It is not that every one cares about this of his or her own private feeling, but the thing has become common ; it is expected of the bereaved, and they get into hot social water with their neighbours if they do not comply. For how many years this has been going on, who can say ? That it will ever end nobody would venture to predict. But even mourning requires a change, and somebody seems to have felt that the good old black edge was getting monotonous, and that something else, equally prominent, might express conventional sorrow. So here we have it—the "New Court Mourning Stationery," "introduced," we are told, "to meet the present day demand for an Artistic Mourning Stationery." It is very simple, very neat, very artistic, very full of sorrow. Just a little pyramid of black up in the left hand corner of the note paper. It is very easily done by drawing a line across the angle and blackening up to both the edges. Let us, at least, welcome any change which gives us less black.

June 11th 1890

REGISTERED UNDER THE
PATENTS, DESIGNS, & TRADE
MARKS ACT, 1888.

Rd. No. 160635.

FAC-SIMILE OF DESIGN
Supplied in all ordinary
sizes of Note Papers.

New Fashionable
COURT · MOURNING · STATIONERY,

SOLE PATENTEES AND MANUFACTURERS.

JOHN DICKINSON & CO LTD.

65 Old Bailey, LONDON, E.C.

MILLS.-CROXLEY, APSLEY, NASH, & HOME PARK,-HERTFORDSHIRE.

To be obtained of all Stationers.

90.7.10,000

[OVER

25. ONE OF THE FIRST DICKINSON ADVERTISEMENTS

June, 1890

26. NASH MILLS (c. 1900)

27. FREDERICK PRATT BARLOW

Chairman, 1886

28. THE ENVELOPE PRINTING ROOM STAFF, APSLEY, 1895

29. LEAVING WORK AT APSLEY, 1905

30. LEWIS EVANS

31. THE NASH MILLS OUTING, 1910

32. UNVEILING THE WAR MEMORIAL, APSLEY MILLS, 1920

33. APSLEY MILLS FROM THE AIR (*c.* 1920)

34. WORKERS' AND MANAGERS' REPRESENTATIVES OF THE
UNION OF THE HOUSE OF DICKINSON, 1926

Timber Hauling on the Seine   From the drawing by L. D. LUARD

Together Boys! — with a strong pull and a long pull — to the certain victory of "Union Year"

R.H.L.

27th January 1927.

Mr. Ellens.

        The attached copy of letter from Mr. Bibby
will doubtless be of interest to you.

Dict. R.H.L.

35. R. H. LING'S LETTERHEAD FOR 1927

36. THE APSLEY BUSES, 1927

37. NEW ENVELOPE BUILDING, APSLEY MILLS, 1927

38. R. H. LING, 1928

39. AFTER LUNCHEON IN THE GUILDHOUSE
Apsley Mills, 1928

40. THE 'R. H. LING' MACHINE, CROXLEY MILLS, 1930

41. SHENDISH: DICKINSON GUILD OF SPORT, 1937

42. SIR REGINALD BONSOR, BART.

Chairman 1933-55

43. 65 OLD BAILEY, 1941

44. A STILL FROM THE FILM
'DICKINSON'S IN BATTLE-DRESS', 1945

45. APSLEY MILLS, THE ENVELOPE FACTORIES BY NIGHT

46. NEW BRIDGE STREET SHOW-ROOMS IN LONDON

47. HOME PARK MILLS

48. THE OLD AND NEW SALLES AT CROXLEY MILLS

49. J. W. RANDALL, MANAGING DIRECTOR 1944–55
Chairman 1955–

John Dickinson & Co. Ltd

MONTREAL
TORONTO
HAMILTON

CYPRU
ALEXANDRIA
CAIRO

NAIRO

SALISBURY
BULAWAYO
JOHANNESBURG
BLOEMFONTEIN
E
CAPE TOWN   POR

Home Bran